MELLOWS

A CHRONICLE OF UNKNOWN SINGERS

By

R. EMMET KENNEDY

Decorations by
SIMMONS PERSONS

ALBERT AND CHARLES BONI
NEW YORK   PUBLISHERS

Printed in the United States of America by
J. J. LITTLE AND IVES COMPANY, NEW YORK

To

FRANCES McKEE TINKER

AND

EDWARD LAROCQUE TINKER,

Friends both,
in the True and Deepest
Meaning of the Name.

FOREWORD

It would appear superfluous to enter into any discussion on the origin, character or musical significance of the Negro spiritual, since the fact is so well established that it is an original lyrical creation of the Afro-American mind evolved in this country, second only in point of time to the song of the Red Man. But a few words may seem necessary in explanation of the name "mellows."

Dialect is not the speech to which the Negro will cling; but for elemental poetry, poignancy and expressiveness it far excels purer speech, and in this his songs have that direct emotional utterance that belongs to all time, making them musical art productions of estimable value. These songs are known throughout the South as spirituals, "himes" and "ballets"; but the "mellows" and "make-up" songs of the Louisiana Negro claim a distinctive place. Mellow is the Negro word for melody, and by this term their devotional songs are called in southern Louisiana. So redolent of this quality are they that we are reminded of the words of Renan, speaking of the Celtic melodies: "Like emanations from above they fall, drop by drop, upon the soul and pass through it like the memories of another world."

CONTENTS

MUSIC INDEX

MELLOWS

HOW they call,
Those spirit voices,
Through the mists of deathless time.
How they charm
The nightly silence
With sweet sounds
For you and me;
Those strange
Familiar voices
Of the dim and distant ages,
Telling Time's impassioned fancies
Wafted on from sea to sea.

What a vast survey of pleasant vistas engages the attention when you take up the history of folk-song and ballad literature. You seem to go back to the very beginning of things, long before literature was;

I

back to a time so remote, you seem to sink into the deathless reverie of oblivion wherein the very names of the authors of this poetry of the people have faded irrevocably.

Among the earliest important collections of old English ballads and broadsheets of which record has been made, the one given first place was the collection made by the antiquarian Anthony a-Wood in 1685. Next in order in æsthetic interest and importance are the "Reliques of Ancient English Poetry," published by Bishop Thomas Percy in 1765; the valuable contributions of Joseph Ritson, "Ancient Songs," "Ancient Popular Poetry" (1791), and the "Robin Hood Garland" (1795). Scottish literature has been enriched likewise by Allan Ramsay's "The Tea-Table Miscellany" (1719), "The Evergreen" (1724); Sir Walter Scott's "Minstrelsy of the Scottish Border" (1803); "The Jacobite Relicks of Scotland" by the Ettrick Shepherd (1819), and William Motherwell's "Minstrelsy Ancient and Modern" (1827). A like memorable service to Irish literature has been rendered by Joseph Walker's "Historical Memoirs of the Irish Bards" (1786); Crofton Croker's "Researches" and "Fairy Legends & Traditions of the South of Ireland" (1825); Douglas Hyde's "Love Songs of Connacht" (1893), and the invaluable music relics of Bunting, Petrie and Joyce. Wales is represented by Edward Jones' "Musical & Poetical Relicks of the Welsh Bards" (1794), and "The Bardic Museum of Primitive British Literature" (1802); Arthur Somervell's "Welsh Melodies," and Alfred Perceval Graves' "Welsh Poetry, Old & New" (1912). And the little Manx nation is adequately represented by the delightful contributions of Dr. Clague and the Deemster Gill.

The American ballad-maker and song-writer, it would seem, never indulged to any great extent in the primitive method of bringing his homely song before the public notice in the form of the broadsheet after the fashion of his Celtic and Anglo-Saxon forebears. Upon examination of the folk-song collections extant it is evident that the early singers did very little in the way of inventive or creative song, rather appearing content to adapt the foreign songs of their ancestors, claiming them as their own after the lapse of a generation or two. Any number of the so-called early American folk-songs can be traced to their English, Irish, Scotch and Welsh originals.

It was not until Stephen Collins Foster began publishing in conventional sheet music form his tender, emotional heart-songs that the ballad had any considerable place in American music literature. The popular ditty and topical song of to-day, with all their vehemence and variegation, have almost succeeded in making the undiscriminating forget the real significance of the venerable word. We sometimes find ourselves trying to delude ourselves into thinking that to-day is not very different from the day of long ago; that the ideals and sentiments of our grandmothers and great-grandmothers were not so radically dissimilar to those of the present, practical, progressive times. But if we consult the song records of the old days, the popular songs voicing the common sentiment of the common people, songs of the heart that awaken the better emotions and help to keep us closer to the things of the spirit, we will recognize an astonishing difference. And we are made to feel happy with the thought that these songs did not die, but timidly sank back into the shadow, embalmed in their own beauty, as it were, to come down to us and help purify the heavy atmosphere of cheap suggestiveness and coarse vulgarity we are obliged to breathe in these ultra modern days.

"Songs from hearts sincere,
Though heard but once in passing,
Touching souls atune,
Can never be forgotten,
Or lost, however simple."

It is a fortunate thing for art and literature that there still remain a few sections of the country where progress has been slow in making her entry, and there remain a few primitive folk who have not got away from being natural and who hold fast to racial characteristics. Conspicuous among these folk are the Negroes of the South. The individuality of their music has awakened interesting comment throughout the country; and the fantastic ideas and naïve expression of many of their spirituals or "ballets" are sufficiently meritorious to have them rank as valuable contributions to the general development of our national lore. Anton Dvorak, sensitive to the great musical worth of the Bohemian airs and Gypsy songs of his native land, instinctively recognized the intrinsic value of these Negro melodies and incorporated some of the motifs in his "New World" symphony. Louis Moreau Gottschalk likewise was impressed with the native charm of the folk melodies of the Louisiana Creoles and utilized some of them to great advantage in his piano transcriptions of the "Bamboula," "La Savane" and "Le Bananier."

For a romantic interpretation of the Negro we are inclined to go back to the picturesque days of the old plantation with its "fiddle-songs," "corn-songs," "devil-songs," jig-tunes, and that most peculiar and interesting custom of all, the "shout," a religious manifestation not unlikely a relic of some native African dance. This shouting was confined to the Baptists, and many of the most beautiful spirituals and "running shouts" are the productions of that denomination, the songs producing the same effect upon their emotional members even in the present day.

Francis Pendleton Gaines, in his book "The Southern Plantation, a Study in the Development and the Accuracy of a Tradition," has given a scholarly analysis in the second chapter which is devoted to "The Development of the Conception of the Plantation in Literature"; the beginning of which he placed between the years 1832 and 1850. He says that the plantation makes its first important appearance in American literature in John Pendleton Kennedy's "Swallow Barn," published in 1832; and in "The Cavaliers of Virginia," by William A. Carruthers, published in 1834.

"Towards the close of this period," Mr. Gaines tells us, "the plantation had so penetrated the American artistic imagination that its echoes are found in unexpected places. Poe is commonly thought of as the author who, more than any other of our native writers, let his fancy indulge in some ethereal dream by some weird, eternal stream. At the same time, however, he brings the Negro character of Jupiter into the story of 'The Gold-Bug" (published in 1843). "However justly this black may be criticized as to dialect or characterization, the fact is before us that Poe realized the appropriateness of placing in his mystery tale a typical devoted house slave on the Southern estate."

Poe was living in Richmond, Va., in 1816, and he went to live in Baltimore, Md., in 1833; during which period of seventeen years he certainly must have accumulated some knowledge of plantation life and have had something like a sympathetic understanding of the poetic and musical sensibilities of the Negroes he saw around him. In *Graham's Magazine* for November, 1843, in his review of James Fenimore Cooper's novel "Wyandotte," Poe says: "The Negroes, without exception, are admirably done."

If we take into consideration Poe's environment during this period in the South,—his extraordinary sensitiveness to tonal beauty, the colorful sound of words, the irresistible lure of music and the rhythm of untrammeled nature, then we need feel no great surprise when we read Edmund Clarence Stedman's hint at another connection between Poe and the plantation. He says: "I have had a fancy that our Southern poet's ear caught the music of 'Annabel Lee' and 'Eulalie,' if not their special quality, from the plaintive, melodious Negro songs utilized by those early writers of 'minstrelsy' who have been denominated the only composers of a genuine American school."

This assertion may contain little of truth and may be somewhat difficult to prove, but we may take it for what it is worth. At any rate, it is of sufficient interest to invite speculation.

Turning to Poe's essay "The Poetic Principle," we read: "Contenting myself with the certainty that Music, in its various modes of meter, rhythm and rhyme, is of so vast a moment in Poetry as never to be wisely rejected—is so vitally important an adjunct, that he is simply silly who declines its assistance." . . . "It is in Music, perhaps, that the soul most nearly attains the great end for which, when inspired by the Poetic Sentiment, it struggles—the creation of supernal beauty." . . . "We are often made to feel, with a shivering delight, that from an earthly harp are stricken notes which cannot have been unfamiliar to the angels."

Then again in the "Philosophy of Composition," he says: "Beauty of whatever kind, in its supreme development, invariably excites the sensitive soul to tears. Melancholy is thus the most legitimate of all the poetical tones."

It was because Poe was so close to Nature and her primal secrets that his poetry has so much of natural magic. And the same thing may be said of the simple, untaught, inspired Negro singers of the Southern plantations, who have created the beautiful devotional songs known as "spirituals." These elevating excitations of the soul are the unconscious productions of Nature's own children filled with a keen sense of primal beauty and the melancholy legacy of longing and loneliness.

Poe also speaks of no other form of poetry having been so universally employed for artistic effect as that of the "refrain." He says: "As commonly used, the refrain, or burden, not only is limited to lyric verse, but depends for its impression upon the force of monotony—both in sound and thought. The pleasure is deduced solely from the sense of identity,—of repetition."

Strangely enough, this is a marked characteristic of Negro spirituals. The burden, or refrain, is sometimes repeated to the extent of producing semi-intoxication or overcoming the sense of the listener very like the effect of a spell or incantation; especially if the spiritual in which it occurs is one of innumerable stanzas, as many of them are. A splendid example of this "force of monotony," with a burden of growing insistence both in sound and thought, is the old spiritual:

O who dat com - in, Tall an - gel at de bar, O

who dat com - in', Tall an - gel at de bar. It

look like Gab - rel Tall an - gel at de bar, It

look like Gab - rel, Tall an - gel at de bar.—

Who dat be - hind him, Tall an - gel at de bar O

who dat be - hind him, Tall an - gel at de bar. O it

look like Je - sus, Tall an - gel at de bar, Yes it

look like Je - sus, Tall an - gel at de bar; Say - in'

blow yo' trum-pet, Tall an - gel at de bar, Gab - rel

blow yo' trum pet, Tall an - gel at de bar.—

Blow it loud as thunduh,
Tall angel at de bar,
Seven claps o' thunduh,
Tall angel at de bar.
Wake de sleepin' nation,
Tall angel at de bar,
All de sleepin' nation,
Tall angel at de bar.

Call de twelve w'ite hawses,
   Tall angel at de bar,
From de hills o' Zion,
   Tall angel at de bar.
Hitch 'um to de cha'yut,
   Tall angel at de bar,
O de golden cha'yut,
   Tall angel at de bar.
Ride up ovuh Jurden,
   Tall angel at de bar,
Thoo de streets o' Jurden,
   Tall angel at de bar.
O bow down, moanuh,
   Tall angel at de bar,
All yo' journey's ovuh,
   Tall angel at de bar.
Take yo' milk an' honey,
   Tall angel at de bar,
Drink de healin' watuh,
   Tall angel at de bar.
O dah's full an' plen'y,
   Tall angel at de bar,
In mah fathuh's mansion,
   Tall angel at de bar.
O dah's room fo' thousan's,
   Tall angel at de bar,
Take yo' seat in glory,
   Tall angel at de bar.

Any number of these spirituals or devotional songs may be taken as examples and you will readily recognize many of the elements enumerated by Poe in his analysis of the Poetic Principle; melancholy, perhaps, the most predominant. Of course if we dissociate the words of these songs from the melodies to which they are wedded, regarding them in the light of cultured poetry, then they must be classed as simple, homely folk-verses possessing a sufficient quality of spontaneous emotion and originality of invention to entitle them to a place in the category of poetic literature. But if we judge them as a whole, musical productions helping to quicken and nourish the pathos and the quiet reverence of the heart, with their remarkable wealth of intricate rhythms and melodious cadences and their admirable unity of sound and sense, then it is not difficult to imagine the effect they might have had on the music-haunted brain of a man like Poe, the helpless victim of exquisite melancholy given to the "luxury of woe," who found the keenest pleasure in making deathless music of his fantastic broodings.

These spirituals, or devotional songs, which have become traditional hymns, were originally extemporaneous; evolved partly under the influence of association with the whites, but in the main, original in the best sense of the word; the inspiration of a moment of ecstasy, the expression of religious elation curiously intermingled with emotion of intrinsically barbaric character; the chanted prayer of a simple child-mind, the melodious cry of a "soul on its knees."

The words are sometimes crude and often meaningless; and again you come across a line of poetic imagery that brings a thrill as pleasing as a line from Chaucer or a pastoral echo from Allan Ramsay's "Gentle Shepherd." The artless sincerity of these songs is the thing which makes them epical in their grandeur and their foolishness.

One of these "ballets" in miniature broadsheet form, telling it was "composed by the Evangelist blind man God sent to warn sons and daughters," has this refrain:

> Good-bye, dear Mother,
>   Your voice will be heard no more.
> Death done summoned her body,
>   Crape is nailed on the door.

Another one called "The Walls Come Tumbling Down," gives this astonishing information:

> Run here, Mitchell, with your key,
>   Unlock the bottomless pit,
> For here is a man he looks so old,
> Believe the Devil done bought his soul.
>   O the wall come tumbling down.

Mitchell and Michael are interchangeable designations to the inspired Negro psalmist and his religious fervor is never deterred by any law of simple rhetoric. Another stanza tells you,

> O I am going to speak in due time;
>   Hope's horse is a horse got tender loins.
> You might ride Hope's horse to-day,
> Next time you ride in Hell to stay.
>   O the wall come tumbling down.

There is another one reading: "Recomposed by the Missionary Rev. F. J. Montgomery of New Orleans, La., better known as the 'World's Battle Ax,'" and it has these thrilling lines:

God got angry on his throne,
He called the angels and they began to mourn;
They dropped their wings and veiled their face,
And cried, have mercy on the human race.

Go down, Angels, consume the flood,
Blow out the sun, turn the moon to blood;
Go down, Angels, and bolt the door,
Times have been shan't be no more.

O come here Angels of bottomless pit
    With a great chain in your hand;
Stop the Devil in his mighty wit
    And bind him at Heaven's command.

This interesting "ballet" is called "Angel Done Gone Down," and is decorated on the reverse side with a picture of the Reverend Battle Ax and the announcement that "This man is like that Stone that was rejected"; probably a reference to Matthew xxi, 42.

Biblical stories form the basis of many of these spirituals and the expounding of them is often illuminating. The most obstinate Scripture lines and phrases of varying lengths and accent are forced to do duty to the same melody with such wonderful skill as to be almost impossible of imitation by a white singer.

There is another one called "When the Ball Was Over," telling how

Herodias went down to the river one day,
Wanted to know what John the Baptist had to say;

John spoke these words at the risk of his life,—
Not lawful to marry your brother's wife.

(Chorus)
>   When the ball was over,
>   When the ball was over,
>   When the ball was over,
>   There was many sad aching hearts.

Herodias got in the chariot and went back home,
Her mind had rested on brother John.
These were the words Herodias spoke and said,—
I am going to get him if it takes me all my days.

Herodias had a daughter by the name of Solom,
The poor little girl she was well known;
She called her daughter in a peculiar way,
What you reckon Herodias did say?

She ran to her mother whooping and crying,
She ran to her mother with her head hung down;
Interesting thoughts were on her mind,
Crying, give me the head of John divine.

Herodias spoke in advance,
I am going to send my daughter out to dance.
Solom was the dancer, she danced very well,
But the dancer liked to dance her soul to hell.

Herodias called these men to come around,—
Come in haste, don't make an alarm;

I have a piece of work for you to do,
Come on, I am going to instruct you.

Caught John the Baptist, laid him on the ground;
The cruel men were standing around;
They looked on John with a frown
While he was laying down on the ground.

In another one called "Sampson Tore the Building Down," in some respects resembling one called "Wasn't That a Witness for My Lord" given in the Calhoun Plantation collection, in that it relates the prowess of the great hero of Bible-story, we have the account of Delilah the temptress told in innumerable stanzas in this graphic manner:

Delilah was a woman that was fine and fair,
Pleasant looking with coal black hair.
Delilah she gained Sampson's mind,
When he first seen the woman she looked so fine.
But did he went to Timothy I can't tell
If the daughter of Timothy pleased him well.
He asked his father to go and see
Can you get that beautiful woman for me?

(Chorus)

If I had my way,
O Lordy, Lordy,
If I had my way;
If I had my way,
I would tear this building down.

Sampson's mother she said to him,
Can't you find a wife among our kin;
She said, O Sampson, it grieves your mother's mind
For you to go and marry to a Philistine.
Now let me tell you what Sampson done,
He broke at the lion and the lion run;
Sampson was the man that the lion attack,
Sampson caught the lion and got on his back.
'Twas written that the lion killed a man with his paw,
But Sampson had his hand in the lion's jaw.

Sampson gave a feast and there came a debate,
He put forth a riddle to interpretate,—
So many garments he said he would give
If they tell his riddle in seven days.

Sampson's feast was almost through,
The known of the riddle was not yet in view.
They called his wife and instruct her what to do,—
Please ask your husband and he'll tell it to you.

She says what is the riddle, please tell it to me,
You said out of the strong came forth the meat;
What is your riddle, please tell it to me,
You said out of the eater came forth the sweet.
I killed a lion, long after he was dead
The bees made honey in the lion's head.

Sampson went in a town and he stayed too late,
They wanted to kill him and they laid in wait.

Tell me, wasn't Sampson awful strong?
He pulled up the gate post and taken them along.

Sampson burned down a field of corn,
They looked for Sampson but he was gone.
So many thousands formed a plot,
Not many days before he was caught.

They bound him with rope while the crowd stood by,
He looked on the ground and then closed his eye.
He just moved his arms, the rope popped like thread,
When he got through slaying three thousand was dead.
O Church, just listen to the tale,
They caught poor Sampson and put him in jail.
Sampson was a man very large in size,
They overpowered the man and plucked out his eyes.

But now, O Church, ain't you glad
To hear what Sampson said to the lad,—
These was the words that Sampson said,
Show me a pillow for to lay my head.

Church, let me tell you what the Philistine done,
They brought Sampson to the building to have some fun.
We are told that the building was high from the ground,
Sampson brisked against the pillow and it tumbled down.

The rhythmic urge and infectious monotony of this stirring canticle with its recurring chorus,

> If I had my way,
> O Lordy, Lordy,

If I had my way,
If I had my way,
I would tear this building down,

succeed in producing on a congregation or a group of singers in a room
an effect beyond description, a state of mental dizziness not soon forgotten.

Another one called "Business Affairs," has this ominous warning:

Go tell that Ball Room Lady
    Get all her business right;
She better get her heart in order
    For the train may be here tonight.

(Chorus)
You must get your business right
For the train may be here tonight;
You must have your ticket ready
For she'll soon be out of sight.

The little black train is coming,
    I know it is going to slack;
You can tell it by its rumbling,
    It's all craped in black.

That train we are singing about
    It has no whistle or bell,
And when you find your station
    You are in Heaven or Hell.

There are men and women
    That love their sport and game,

Yet death is riding with them,
Will take them just the same.

The rich man in grandeur
Filled with his worldly ways,
Said I will build my barns a little larger
And live for many days.

But that very night the king of terror came,—
Said, rich old man thy judgment's come;
This very night thy soul must be
At judgment bar and throne.

Another one called "Elder Ain't You Got a Mission?" has this declaration of thankfulness:

I got my soul converted,
I put on my gospel shoe;
And if I can't sing like angels,
I know I got a mission, too.

Modern progress and cold commercialism too frequently perform lamentable feats in the way of obliterating old forms and destroying sentimental and æsthetic values regardless of their historic worth. Thus the charm of a picturesque old culture slowly fades away. Generations pass out and custom takes on a new guise, and only occasionally in some obscure corner remnants of an old tradition will linger in the memory of a few sentimental souls who treasure the things of the long ago. Nowhere, perhaps, is this fact more fully demonstrated than in New Orleans, that distinctive city of cosmopolitanism and indigenous nationalities—descendants of Spanish Dons, French noblemen, Acadian refugees, Creole aristocrats, Choctaw Indians, Irish and German fortune-hunters, Manila and Negro cross-breeds—each one retaining many of its racial provincialisms and customs that make a harmonious composite pattern expressing America though virtually un-American.

If you have ever been to that romantic old city on a visit you will remember what a peculiar charm the Vieux Carré exerted over you, with its intrusive dialects and diatribes, colors and cobblestones, Moorish balconies overhanging the banquettes or sidewalks, where mysterious court-yards bloom behind great postern-like doors with curious iron gratings that flirt with you invitingly; where blue mosaic street names appear at every corner inlaid in the pavement; where prolific wistaria and Madeira vines send down their luscious odors from second-story galleries trellised with iron lacework; and where waxen looking yucca plants, banana trees and date palms greet you with a tropic welcome from nearly every front garden, be it ever so small.

It may be this same charm is somewhat commonplace to one who has lived there for many years, simply because he knows that it is not confined exclusively to the old French Quarter, and that its influence can be felt in other parts of the city as well; even in that district above Canal Street which the old-time Creole aristocrat refers to disdainfully as the "Americaine section."

Among the many quaint old customs which still prevail there, perhaps the most characteristic is the going about of the Negro street vendors with their plaintive, melodious cries by which they announce their wares. Many of the old families still adhere to the time-honored custom of having the weekly washing done in the back yards, thereby enabling the clothes-pole man to continue plying his simple trade, making his periodical visits to town with a bundle of long white ash clothes-poles on his shoulder. His cry is a sort of spasmodic ejaculation given in loud, deep tones:

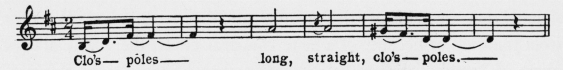

Clo's— poles——   long, straight, clo's— poles.——

Several times a week the buttermilk man comes around with his large can of buttermilk, walking all the way from his little dairy out on Telemachus Street, across the Basin, in the "back-of-town" section of the city. His cry is one of chromatic pleading, enticing you to buy in spite of yourself:

But-ter - milk——   But-ter - milk——

The selling of hot potato-cakes seems to be the exclusive prerogative of women. These cakes are made of sweet potatoes, though occasionally they are made of Irish potatoes, and they are sold hot. Whether from tradition or because of a better musical effect, the cry is always given in "gombo" French, the patois spoken by the Creole Negroes. These vendors are heard mostly down in the French Quarter around nightfall. And it is very soothing to your mental condition on a hot August night when you are sitting in your room sizzling in unstudied negligée, trying to pacify yourself with the aid of a palmetto fan and a pitcher of cold lemonade with tamarinds in it, to hear the potato-cake woman go by in the street below singing:

Bel pam pa - tat, Bel pam pa - tat, Ma-
dam, ou - lay - ou le bel pam pa - tat, pam pa - tat.

Then along in the early part of the month of May, the blackberry woman comes to town with her belated spring-song. Her call is full of melancholy poetry which seems to tell you that she has been up since the "crackin' o' day," picking blackberries in the woods and along the bayou banks, and that she has walked miles and miles over dew-wet, dusty, country roads in order to get to town to sell her berries before noon. You are assured of this when you see her with her basket of berries on her head, the dew and the berry juice dripping from the basket and running down her back in purple rillets. The basket is covered with sprays of elder and sycamore leaves to protect the berries from the heat of the sun. On her head, serving as a cushion under the basket, she has a "tosh," formed of an old garment of some kind which has been twisted and coiled, resembling a sort of thick mat. Her skirt is tucked up gypsy-fashion all around her waist, and her dusty shoes and bare legs show every trace of long travel. Perhaps it is due to her weariness of body that her cry has a suggestion of melancholy:

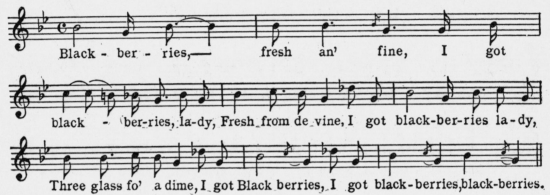

Black - ber - ries,—— fresh an' fine, I got black - ber-ries, la-dy, Fresh from de vine, I got black-ber-ries la-dy, Three glass fo' a dime, I got Black berries, I got black-berries, black-berries.

Then in the autumn, when the crows come back from the fields of the North, the chimney-sweeper comes around to remind people that their chimneys need cleaning before the coming of winter. His dress is traditional, in strict accordance with the chimney-sweeper's idea of correct convention. He wears a top hat, a long linen duster, and over his shoulder he carries a bundle of sacks and ropes and long brushes made from the frayed leaves of the palmetto. He calls himself "Rom-ma-nay," which is "gombo" French for the word "ramoneur," meaning chimney-sweeper. He comes along singing in a loud voice:

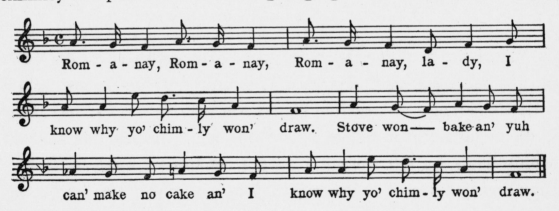

Rom - a - nay, Rom - a - nay, Rom - a - nay, la - dy, I know why yo' chim - ly won' draw. Stove won—— bake an' yuh can' make no cake an' I know why yo' chim - ly won' draw.

The charcoal man has no special season. His visits are usually twice a week, as charcoal is in constant demand by the washerwomen who do "de w'ite-folks washin' an' i'nin' on de primisis."

There was a man who used to go around with an old white mule and a rickety spring wagon, and his cry was like this:

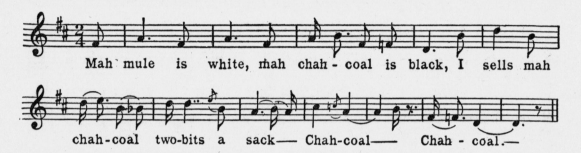

Mah mule is white, mah chah-coal is black, I sells mah chah-coal two-bits a sack— Chah-coal— Chah-coal.—

The exercise of singing, the common heritage of all simple people who live close to nature, is not only delightful but helpful to preserve the health and good spirits of man. Byrde, a prominent organist and composer of Queen Elizabeth's time, says of singing: "It doth strengthen all parts of the breast, and doth open the pipes. It is the only way to know where Nature hath bestowed the benefit of a good voice. The better the voice is, the meeter it is to honour and serve God therewith.

Since singing is so good a thing,
I wish all men would learn to sing."

Nature has been especially kind to the Negro in bestowing upon him the gift of song at all times. And as long as he remains true to this priceless heritage he has from his African ancestors we can feel happy in the thought that it will be a long time before the haunting glamour of this delightful folk-life will disappear completely and leave that romantic section barren of itinerant singers and traditional work-songs echoing so poetically the common life of the people; work and play, suffering and sorrow, laughter, love and death,—the worst as well as the best of life expressed in music. Hardship and privation run into melody from the lips of these people as naturally as the scent of the clover blossom flows out over the field. A girl hanging up clothes on a washline, an old granny sitting under a persimmon tree picking moss, men tugging at a raft of logs in a muddy canal, a boy at a mill-pond washing a wagon load of carrots for market, an old man calling a flock of scattered chickens for their evening meal, a young woman helping to paint a cypress box that is to hold the body of her dead child,—such are the things that move these elemental folk to song as naturally as the coming of day sets the roosters to crowing or the June moonlight wakens the mocking bird to holy rapture.

Peace of mind, a resigned spirit and a cheerful imagination are often the means of making a song to serve a good purpose out of the merest material. Let us listen to a group of women in a bean field where they are picking butterbeans for market. They are ranged in rows down the long aisles of glossy bean vines growing on upright cane-reed poles placed like the ribs of an Indian's tepee. They have been at work since sunrise and it is nearing time for resting. One woman takes the lead, singing each line of the chant alone, the other women forming the chorus singing in unison with perfect rhythm and sympathy. The leader's mind is a medley of reminiscences, and thinking aloud, she fits her fancies to a plaintive melody, the other women falling in at most unexpected intervals and supplying the different harmonies with musicianship that is bewildering. The song has a naïvete that is charming as it lures a handful of butterbeans from each one of them to be emptied into the basket with every cadence:

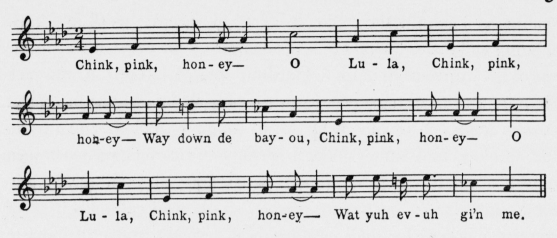

Chink, pink, honey,
   O Lula,
Chink, pink, honey,
   One ole faded hankchuh.

Chink, pink, honey,
   O Lula,
Chink, pink, honey,
   Washed it in de bayou.

Chink, pink, honey,
   O Lula,
Chink, pink, honey,
   Fade all ove' de bayou.

Chink, pink, honey,
   O Lula,
Chink, pink, honey,
   My mothuh tol' me.

Chink, pink, honey,
   O Lula,
Chink, pink, honey,
   Gawd won' fuhsake me.

And on and on the song goes until her fancy is exhausted and the baskets are filled and the bean-picking ends.

These work-songs are human documents of the Negro's self-expression of the great rhythms of life. His labor is always a pleasure as long as he is able to rhythmize it in song and keep his companions singing and working in unison. Listen to the crude, disjointed chant of a small group of men working on a railroad track. They are dragging out the old worn crossties and putting in new ones under the rails. The leader sings a line and they all fall to and take hold of the crosstie; then he sings another line and they give a tug at the crosstie, and with every line chanted another tug, until the crosstie is in place. After each line the leader gives a short ejaculation, a sort of melodious grunt, "Umph," without interrupting the rhythm in the slightest degree:

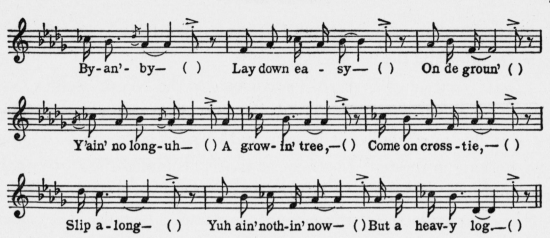

By-an'- by— ( ) Lay down ea - sy— ( ) On de groun' ( )

Y'ain' no long-uh— ( ) A grow- in' tree,—( ) Come on cross-tie,— ( )

Slip a - long— ( ) Yuh ain' noth-in' now— ( )But a heav-y log.—( )

What a picture of pulsing life it gives, with its native sense of syncopation and glint of poetic fancy. The picture of the stately cypress tree that was, growing in the lonely swamp with all its feathery green branches draped in trailing grey moss, surrounded on all sides by tall sycamores and spreading live oak trees that sang gloriously when the wind went over them; now nothing but the semblance of a tree transformed into a plain, commonplace cross-tie, lying ignobly on the ground waiting to be dragged under the iron rail of the track, far away from the scene of its departed glory with every suggestion of beauty lost forever.

In the matter of repetition and monotony many of these impromptu ditties seem to have a certain relationship to that variety of accumulative song found in the whimsical jingles attributed to good old Mother Elizabeth Foster Goose of Boston town. They sometimes suggest a picture of simple, peaceful home life full of the satisfaction that means so much to the humble heart unaccustomed to big things. This is illustrated in a work-song of men "tamping" cinders under the crossties after they have been secured in place under the rails. The men all work in unison, each one with a long iron "tamp," a kind of crowbar with a spatulated nose. With the first line of the chant, "By an' by," they all lift their tamps together, letting them fall on the last word, giving two falls to the beat and raising them again on the "By an' by" of the second line; continuing with unvarying rhythm to let the tamps fall on the right accent, the accented words of the third line being "lay," "won't" and "tall." The chant is short but it succeeds admirably in presenting a clear picture of the Negro's introspective mind:

-by— By-an'- by— O by-an'- by— I'm gwine look all ov-uh

yond-ah by-an'- by— By-an'- by— Sweet by-an' - by—

— Gawd gwine bet-tuh My cun - dis - hun by- an' - by.—

Sometimes a lovely "song without words" floats into being, virtually carrying no special meaning but helping to hasten the conception of a fanciful reverie. I recall a drowsy, balmy Sunday afternoon in September. The windows were open and a light, soothing breeze was blowing, carrying with it the mingled odors of China-berry and honey-suckle flowers, making the room where I sat reading a bower of sensuous sweetness. There was also the sound of melody on the breeze; fitful, wistful melody that made you think of the "sleepy music," the "soontree" spoken of in the fanciful legends of Pagan Ireland. It was so haunting and importunate that I got up to see where the sound came from, and just outside the window in the shade of the camphor tree growing on the banquette there was a young colored man sitting on the soft grass, with his feet across the gutter. He had a twig in his hand and he was raking the scattered camphor leaves into a pile, whistling his melancholy chant over them very like a lyric grasshopper lamenting the departure of summer. It was a mysterious whistle-tune, full of poignant, untranslatable poetry. I have preserved the song, but its meaning, like the name of the whistler, has yet to be learned:

In making the settings of these songs and spirituals it is my desire to give faithful transcriptions as my memory recorded the singing of the Negroes of my native town. Some of them were taken down at first hearing, sometimes with slight variations if sung by more than one singer. I have tried to follow as closely as I know how the intuitive harmonies and instinctive rhythmic peculiarities of these musical people, and have tried to suggest in the accompaniments the primitive, rudimental element so marked in all their productions.

In nearly all the Negro churches these spirituals are sung without any accompanying instrument, a fact which may cause these settings to appear rather sudden transitions from the simple folk stage to something akin to the art song. It is not my intention to destroy the character or mar the import of the songs by presenting them with seeming modern accompaniments, which in my opinion not only emphasize the beauty of the melodies, but are intended to suggest the remarkable voice harmonies and tonal atmosphere which make these songs so distinctive when sung by their gifted creators.

The words are given in the Negro dialect and should be sung without any attempt to transform them into correct English or make them resemble in any way the conventional art song, whereby their picturesque quality and racial character will be utterly lost and they will become meaningless. They should be sung according to folk-song traditions, with strict attention to rhythm, time, accentuation, judicious stress, and just conception of the sentiments and emotion prompted by the words.

The inspired Negro singer knows little or nothing about tone production, breath control, correct attack, bel canto or free enunciation, yet he sings these moving chants of religious ecstasy in a manner almost impossible of imitation by a trained singer. His song is of a natural order, full of genuine feeling, opening its way directly to the general heart. Those who look forward to the development of African talent in the field of music, and those who love these songs for the songs' sake, even though they cannot sing them, can keep fresh their friendly interests for these people and help their petitions for the approach of the time when they shall rejoice in their just portion.

An interesting old book called "A South-Side View of Slavery," published in 1854 by the Rev. Nehemiah Adams, concludes with the following apostrophe to the music of the American Negro: "If the nations of the earth celebrate in heaven their national experiences under the providence and grace of God, Africa's song will probably do as much as any to illustrate them. But who will write Africa's hymn? What mysteries of providence and grace, what remembrances of woe, what corresponding heights of joy and bliss, what forgiveness and love, what adoration, what sweet affections born of chastisement, what appreciation of heaven, with its liberty and equality and recompense of patient suffering, will that hymn contain, and with what voices will it be sung! No man can learn that song, no man can write it, but some African slave. We from America shall listen to that song with feelings unlike those of any other nation."

The grand hymn remains to be written, perhaps; but who among us has not given his full attention and experienced a thrill of poignant pleasure when listening to any of these lesser songs of these unknown singers, feeling a certain pride in claiming them as art productions of his native land?

As a Southerner, I am happy to offer this collection as an individual contribution interpreting the poetic and melodic natures of the Negro singers of Louisiana.

R. E. K.

ROCK MOUNT SINAI

COME, and walk with me in memory
Through the silent, twilight vistas
Where the spirit holds communion,
Making truthful self-revealment;
Come with me and tread the vistas
With your ears attuned to soundings
Of the old familiar voices
That awake from out the past.

Come, and hear them quick reviving,
All the varied recollections,—
Days of peace and days pathetic,
From youth's distant Lethe calling
Soft as wind among the thistles,—
Come and hear them, feel them, know them,
All the old familiar voices
That seduced my soul with music
In the days of long ago.

My earliest recollection of Negro spirituals carries me back to the pleasant, picturesque days of my seventh year and the eventful beginning of the year 1885, the Annus Mirabilis of my awakening mind: the year that saw the opening of the great Exposition in New Orleans, when "President Arthur surrounded by his cabinet and members of the diplomatic corps, the President of the Senate, Speaker of the House and many other distinguished people, formally opened the Exposition and started its ponderous engine and machinery by pressing a button, and the electric current passing over 1,200 miles of wire became the means by which the chief of our government put into operation the World's Industrial & Cotton Centennial Exposition;" the year that recorded the death of President Ulysses S. Grant and the imposing funeral ceremonies held in so many of the large cities of the Union,—a thing incongruous and wholly unintelligible to my unsophisticated mind; the year that brought the big crevasse, when the treacherous waters of the Mississippi River rose to so great a height the levee was unable to withstand the pressure, causing it to break and let the raging waters rush in and inundate the land for many miles distant. The bayous and canals back of the town of Gretna were soon filled with water and it was not long before the spreading flood backed up through the woods and pasture lands and overflowed the whole town, in some places as high as five feet or more. Any number of families were forced to leave their homes and seek shelter up in the front part of town. Those remaining, the greater number being colored families, were obliged to build false-floors just above the water mark and live marooned and far from being comfortable until the water receded.

As previous experience had shown such floods to be from three to four months' duration, my family hurried away from our little old house which stood quite near to the ground, and moved to a place of safety up toward the front of the village. This exodus by no means interfered with the pleasure and excitement the high-water occasioned. Skiff parties were almost a nightly occurrence; and after much pleading and more loud complaining at being left behind if my mother went, her indulgent heart would respond and I would be permitted to go along.

The memories of those romantic moonlight rides are more like dream fancies than actual experiences. The weird, long journeys out over the town with its forlorn looking houses blinking their oil lamp and candle lighted windows at you as you glided by stealthily in your great skiff under the numerous plank-walks and Japanesque-looking bridges high over the water, leading from one house to the other; the doleful sound of mewed up dogs barking at each other from their lonely confinement; the winding in and out among the trees on the edge of the woods, with the soft smell of button-ball and wild honey-suckle and coral trumpet-flower set afloat by the swishing oars that chased the shivering shadows of mossy branches as they danced on the face of the water in the clear moonlight; the eerie tinkle of the guitars and the merry mocking echo of the voices singing "Evangeline" and "Darling Chloe" and "The Cows Are in the Corn," as we glided through the Hook & Ladder Cemetery high up over the graves and among the tomb tops shining white and ominous in the light of the summer moon; the pathetic pictures of Negro families sitting out on their front galleries, the rude false-floors just a few inches above the water line, with an old shovel or a battered dishpan filled with smoldering rags to smoke off the mosquitoes as they sat there resignedly singing with impressive confidence, "Angel Done Changed My Name."

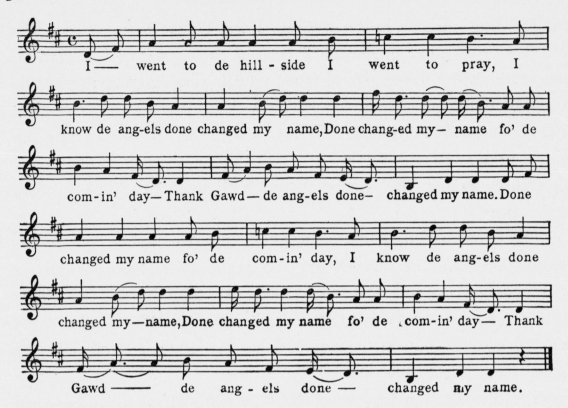

I—went to de hill-side I went to pray, I know de ang-els done changed my name, Done chang-ed my—name fo' de com-in' day—Thank Gawd—de ang-els done— changed my name. Done changed my name fo' de com-in' day, I know de ang-els done changed my—name, Done changed my name fo' de com-in' day— Thank Gawd——de ang-els done—— changed my name.

> I looked at my hands an' my hands were new,
> I know de angels done changed my name;
> I looked at my feet an' my feet were too,
> Thank Gawd de angels done changed my name.

Episodes such as these leave impressions on a child's mind which in after years he remembers with wonder and gladness.

It was also the year that witnessed the miraculous rescue of my apparently drowned body from a well in the yard, where fully five minutes after I had fallen in, my mother pulled me up from the bottom with the aid of a long-handle garden hoe, having been attracted to the spot by the strange behavior of two pet cats that sat by the well-side intently watching the bubbles rise and burst on the surface of the water. Due to her almost insane determination and unceasing effort from nine in the morning until six in the evening, I was at last resuscitated. The memory of my three or four days' term of convalescence is a glorious one in the way of offerings of fruits and flowers and sweetmeats and friendly and curious visitors; and more than all, the lofty satisfaction I experienced in being able to tell everybody that "there was none alligators in the well,"—a frightful myth which had been held up for my protection against the waters of the well as far back as I could remember.

The years of childhood that followed this remarkable episode, extending even into the years of ripe adolescence, were years of rigid circumspection enjoyable only at odd intervals,—an indifferent enjoyment at best,—for it is far from being a comforting thought during one's formative years to feel that one is being constantly guarded like the queen's jewels after the parade. Nevertheless it proved valuable in respect to there having been selected for me two such joyous and devoted companions as the two little colored boys living next door, the sons of Aunt Julie Sparks, our cook and washerwoman.

Aunt Julie's mother, old Aunt Milleete Narcisse, had been a slave on one of the plantations up in the Parishes, and Aunt Julie inherited from her the quick wit, droll humor and genial disposition which give the Creole Negroes the marked distinction they enjoy. Her boys, Sammy and Johnny, reflected many of the qualities of their mother plus excess energy, fertile imagination and all the attributes of efficiency to be desired in a playmate and a companion. Looking back to those days with the rich crop of memories I can wake from them, I feel like that good old Japanese poet of the Meiji Era when he said,

> *"Within the country*
> *Hamlets, God be praised, to-day*

Still linger, here and
There, the simple, sweet old ways
In homes old-fashioned."

Nothing could be more appropriate for the musical setting of my first heard Negro spirituals sung *ensemble* than Sunday morning at Putney Ward's New Hope Baptist Church in Gretna. The least important though most intrusive figure is a curious, impatient little boy standing on a high-chair in the kitchen door and looking out over a long stretch of back-yard, beyond which stands the little old church. The back window of the church is open, and through it the little boy is eagerly watching his playmates, Sammy and Johnny, who have gone to Sunday school with their mother. Aunt Julie is standing near the open window with her two sons, and their voices ring out with welling gladness as they sing the triumphant "shout" called, "Free At Last":

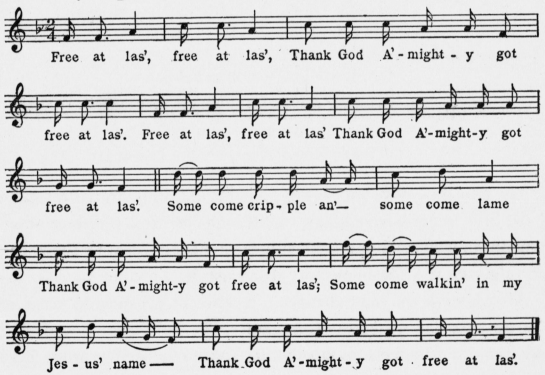

On my knees wen de light pass'd by,
    Thank Gawd A'mighty got free at las',
Thought my soul would rise an' fly,
    Thank Gawd A'mighty got free at las'.

(Chorus)   Free at las', etc.
    Way down yondah in de grave-yahd walk,
        Thank Gawd A'mighty got free at las',
    Me an' my Jesus goin' a-meet an' talk,
        Thank Gawd A'mighty got free at las'.

(Chorus)   Free at las', etc.
    Some o' these mawnin's bright an' fair,
        Thank Gawd A'mighty got free at las',
    Goin' a-meet King Jesus in de air,
        Thank Gawd A'mighty got free at las'.

(Chorus)   Free at las', etc.
    Mah Jesus tol' me once befo',
        Thank Gawd A'mighty got free at las',
    To go in peace an' sin no mo',
        Thank Gawd A'mighty got free at las'.

The two little boys sing lustily, looking the while in the direction of the little white boy standing on his high-chair in a transport of admiration, bravely trying to sing with them. It is a charmed moment, carrying with it a dream-memory that must last a lifetime.

After a while the song changes. A wave of melancholy seems to float up from the struggles of the past. The little white boy doesn't understand but he feels intuitively that something strange must have happened to put so much sadness in their voices, and he finds himself wanting to cry as he tries to sing with them:

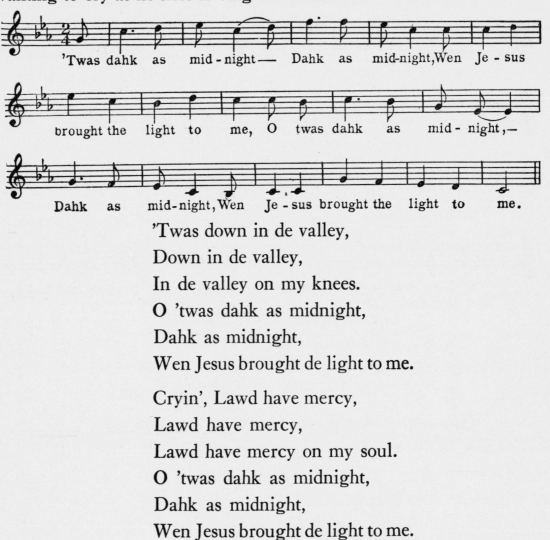

'Twas dahk as mid-night— Dahk as mid-night,Wen Je-sus brought the light to me, O twas dahk as mid-night,— Dahk as mid-night,Wen Je-sus brought the light to me.

'Twas down in de valley,

Down in de valley,

In de valley on my knees.

O 'twas dahk as midnight,

Dahk as midnight,

Wen Jesus brought de light to me.

Cryin', Lawd have mercy,

Lawd have mercy,

Lawd have mercy on my soul.

O 'twas dahk as midnight,

Dahk as midnight,

Wen Jesus brought de light to me.

Aunt Julie looks out of the window and smiles, and Sammy waves his hand to the little white boy. Just then all the Sunday school members begin singing jubilantly:

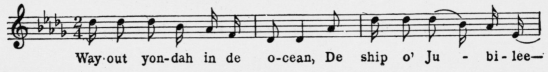

Way out yon-dah in de o-cean, De ship o' Ju - bi-lee—

Mah Lawd Gawd Je-sus is de cap-tain, An' 'e com-in' o-vuh fo' me.— O mah Lawd Gawd rock-in' in de wear-y lan'. in de wear-y lan'— in de wear-y lan.— O mah Lawd Gawd rock-in in de wear-y lan'.— Com-in' to car-ry mah soul to mah Je-sus, Com-in' fo' to car-ry mah soul to mah Lawd.

Git on boahd de ship o' Zion,
　　Be in has'e an' be in min',
O de ship is at de landin'
　　An' I don' wan' leave yuh behin'.

(Chorus)　Mah Lawd Gawd rockin', etc.

Do yuh think that she is able
　　To reach to de heavenly sho'?
She has landed many a thousan'
　　An' will land as many mo'.

(Chorus)　Mah Lawd Gawd rockin', etc.

O de ole ship come a-rockin',
　　A-sailin' ovuh de foam;
She is loaded down wid angels
　　Comin' to carry me home.

(Chorus)　Mah Lawd Gawd rockin', etc.

Like an interrupted dream of happiness, the song comes to a sudden ending.   But the little boy is not sorry, because he knows that Sunday school is almost over, and as soon as Sammy and Johnny get home and have taken off their "good clothes" and copper-toed shoes and Balbriggan stockings they all can eat some of the cinnamon cake and fresh purple figs left from breakfast and then go and play at hide-and-seek out in the pasture among the tall indigo stalks and cocklebur bushes where the geese like to take their little goslings to hide from the glare of the sun.

Then there was chasing of toad frogs in the violet borders and making them prisoners in wide-mouth pickle bottles and charging a pin or a button to look at them.   And catching great red-and-black "devil-horses" you could always find on the jimson-weed bushes, to hitch them up with bridles of thread and make them pull paper match boxes from one end of the gallery to the other.   And gathering hats full of persimmon blossoms from the ground under the trees, to string on thread to wear around your neck until evening, when they withered and all their pleasant fragrance was gone.   And hunting for snake eggs about the roots of the sycamore trees, and when you got tired, sitting down in the shade to watch the turkey buzzards loping around and doing eccentric dances about the carcass of an old cow.   And the rare delight of catching crawfish in the deep puddle in the green out by old Uncle Sawney's house, and listening to Johnny sing:

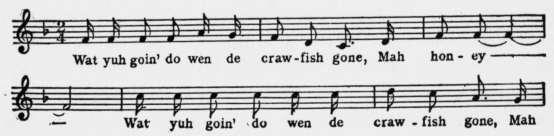

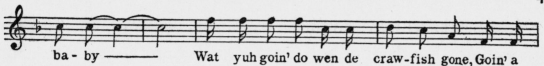

ba - by ——— Wat yuh goin' do wen de craw-fish gone, Goin' a

thro' my line— in de craw-fish pon', Mah hon-ey. ———

Wat yuh goin' do wen de meat give out,
    Mah honey?
Wat yuh goin' do wen de meat give out,
    Mah baby?
Wat yuh goin' do wen de meat give out?
Goin' stan' on de cawnduh wid mah mouf poked out,
    Mah honey.

Grease mah heel wid de hog-eye lahd,
    Dis mawnin';
Grease mah heel wid de hog-eye lahd
    Dis mawnin';
Grease mah heel wid de hog-eye lahd,
Went slippin' an' slidin' thoo de w'ite-folks yahd,
    Mah honey.

Then when night came, and the moon rose over the pasture from behind the clump of tall water willows along the canal bank, and you
knew that romping time was over, and you began to hope that Mr.
Witte, the village blacksmith, would come down for an evening visit
and bring his fiddle and his two little daughters along with him,—then
what a carnival of merriment and childish jubilation! Mr. Witte's repertoire was rich and seductive in German dance tunes; and my father
had a constitutional failing for joyous Irish jigs and reels and one lone

American break-down he called "Natchez Under the Hill," which he had learned when he served as corporal in the Confederate Army. His attachment for his fiddle was almost as great as his fondness for his children, for it had brought him a great share of comfort through many a night of hardship and loneliness during the long struggle, helping him to see the "lighter side of grief" and feel the "laughter that lies so close to tears," and enabling him to express the nameless yearning of his Tipperary temperament. It was a lovely old instrument he bought for a few dollars from a poor sailor, and in the hands of a master would proudly live up to the name of violin and the imposing inscription it bore inside,—

> JOSEPH GUARNERIUS
>
> CREMONA, *1792*

but in my father's hands it was only a "fiddle," though to our childish way of thinking, an enchanted one.

Very often my mother would dance with us, and these two fathers, taking turn about with the music-making, would play until their repertoires were exhausted. Nine o'clock was the hour appointed for all merriment to cease, and we children always knew when the hour had arrived when we saw my father take the middle of the floor and begin to perform with great flourish a most pretentious and melodious lilt, which in after years I learned was a chorus air from the opera Freischutz, very much more conventional than his free rendering of it.

Another privilege was being permitted to go over and sit with Sammy and Johnny when Aunt Julie and Jim and Aunt Charity came out and sat on their front gallery in the moonlight to sing those strangely impressive melodic modulations of the utmost beauty, those "make-up" songs which seem to have come by spontaneous generation out of remote minds from regions more remote.

According to Aunt Julie's calculation, she was a girl about thirteen "wen de firs' gun fo' peace shot off." She said she "was toatin' de din-nuh dishes to de pantry wen de gun went off, an' de thing frighten me so I dropped all de w'ite-folks toys an' broke 'um half-in-two."

Aunt Julie's voice was a warm, colorful mezzo with the extraordinary range peculiar to her race. I have known passers-by to stop outside her gate and listen to her singing, so enthralled were they by its arresting sweetness and emotional depth. I have never heard any one sing Rock Mount Sinai as she did.

She is an old woman now, and although her voice has deepened and taken on a darker color, the true spirit and native art still remain. On a recent visit to her home, upon asking her to sing something for me, she said she did not care to sing by herself but would call her grand-daughter, Zora, "one de henchmen o' de choir," and get her to help. Zora started the melody, Aunt Julie falling in and leaving off as her fancy pleased her, striking an octave above or below with equal ease, and producing the effect of a marvellous complication and variety. Their singing of the following fragment of "make-up" song, all they could remember without the printed "ballet," brought tears of regret and sweet tears of childish remembrance to my eyes:

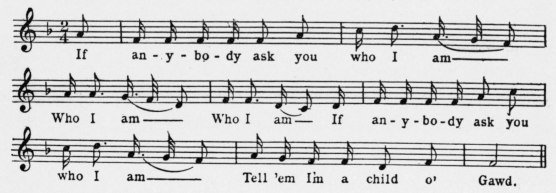

If an-y-bo-dy ask you who I am——
Who I am—— Who I am— If an-y-bo-dy ask you
who I am—— Tell 'em I'm a child o' Gawd.

ROCK MOUNT SINAI

Rock Mount Si - nai, Rock Mount Si - nai, in de - maw - nin'.

Final ending

2nd & 3rd verse

Come on Mo - ses, (m - m - m) Don't you get los' (m - m - m)
Da - vid Da - vid, (m - m - m) A shep - ud boy (m - m - m)

Smote de wa - tuh (m-m-m-m) An' come a - cross (m-m-m-m) O
Killed Go li ah. (m-m-m-m) An' shout - ed fo' joy (m-m-m-m) O

Man of sor - ruh. (m- m-m-m) Sin - nuh don't you see (m - m - m)
Wen I reach hea - v'n (m-m-m-m) Goin' to set right down (m - m)

Died fo' you (m-m-m-m) An'— died fo' me (m-m-m-m) O
An' ask my Lawd (m-m-m-m) Fo' a star - ry crown. (m-m-m) O

DRY BONES

WHEN George Riley was still in his "teens" and full of the exuberant spirits that go with those years, the position he occupied in the family might be called something akin to that of domestic jester. He was by nature a merry-andrew, so it was very easy for him to assume the duty of being cheerful at all times and ready to furnish amusement for the family on any occasion. After the manner of the court jester of the good old days, he was quick to select his especial patron for whom he would perform his merriest antics and recite his rarest conceits,—that fortunate person being none other than my indulgent self. There were just a few years' difference in our ages and we had been playmates from childhood, so there was no restraint or formality or unnecessary decorum to hamper the feeling of natural sympathy and understanding existing between us. His sense of the ridiculous was keen and delightful, and having a full appreciation of the gift, I showed him willing encouragement whenever there was need. His thought for my welfare was more than mere consideration, and his desire for companionship or "comp'ny-keepin'," as he called it, was a form of simple devotion.

The "big house" was home to him; and to be able to declare himself "joint-arran" (joint-heir) of the family to any one who asked about the connection was a thing of great moment to him. If there was a jaunt to the woods after crawfish or Maypops or "pottashaws," George always went along as merry-maker; or if there was a trip to the plantation after blackberries, he would hitch up Balaam the donkey and lead the procession in the jumper as mascot, performing every variety of clown trick to the great amusement of the party. If there was a gathering of any kind at the house during the social season, he was eager to be in evidence "spreadin' joy" and "makin' welcome wid de 'freshnin's" (refreshments). And if a casual visitor happened to call unexpectedly at any hour of the day, he was sure to be on hand almost as soon as the visitor was seated, presenting a "palmeetuh fan" and a glass of cold lemonade,—an attention inaugurated by himself.

On cold winter nights he was blissfully happy if he would be permitted to spread his pallet on the floor before the great open fireplace in my bedroom, where he would wrap himself in his blanket and stretch out before the banked-up fire of odorous magnolia burs lighting the room with a pale, weird blue-and-green light, telling some funny story or singing some moving spiritual until he was silenced by "Miss Ellen's" repeated admonition from the adjoining room, declaring that it was time to go to sleep.

During the hot summer months the attic of the "big house" was the coolest spot to be found. This attic ran the full length of the house and was reached by a long dark stairway opening from the kitchen. It was a spacious, unfinished place with two large windows at the front and two at the back, admitting a free current of air nearly all the time. It had an inviting old room at the end, partitioned off with queer trellis-like walls of unpainted cypress. During old plantation days this room had served as a wine room, and it had long rows of shelves with holes for the bottles to fit in, where they were placed neck-down, after being filled from the cask of claret imported from France once a year. This room had long since lost caste and was now serving as a kind of inferior family museum, with an accumulation of ante-bellum magazines and sheet music, paper-back premium novels of the Once a Week period of literature, odd bottles and quaint jugs and demijohns, distinguished old dresses of poplin and watered silk, disreputable ornaments of French bisque and Bohemian glass, framed offerings of fish-scale flowers and "refined mottoes" worked in zephyr worsted, fascinating strings of sea shells and "charm-buttons" and other refugees from the honorable corner whatnot, decrepit pieces of old furniture too bad to give away and "too redolent of tender memories to destroy," several skeleton-like hoop-skirts and "tiltirinas" of the polonaise period, and a mysterious plaster cast supposed to be the original of the Antomarchi death-mask of Napoleon, the presence of which was a nightly torment to George if he happened to go to the attic alone. Perhaps the most picturesque feature of the place was the extraordinary array of cobwebs and mud-dauber nests forming the mural decoration of the rafters, braces and high shingle roof, the removal of which would mean the passing of romance and mystery hiding behind them.

From out the plenitude of derelict "plunder," as George called it, he helped me to arrange at the front of the attic temporary warm weather sleeping-quarters rather unique and inviting. The view from the large windows was out over a lovely stretch of garden luxuriant with jonquils, Chinese laurel, cape jasmine, camellia japonicas, magnolia fuscati, deadly nightshade, coral honeysuckle, mariposa lilies, and many other varieties of summer flowering plants whose rich odors would rise at night and flow through the queer old attic, making it reek with an atmosphere of such dulcet fragrance and stimulating witchery you felt like one wandering lazily through an unknown region of half-remembered dreams.

It was delightful to lie in bed on a moonlight night and look out across the garden and watch the boats go by on the river about a quarter of a mile away; and watch the reflection of the electric lights on the water trying to zig-zag their way across from the New Orleans side nearly a mile distant, seeming to carry with them the echo of the noisy Tchoupitoulas Street cars bumping along the river front on their way uptown.

The crickets and katydids also liked the sensuous atmosphere of the old attic; but they were too prodigal with their nightly serenading to be appreciated by the loquacious George, who, partly from fear of being left alone downstairs and partly from his inordinate love of company, had pitched his cot on one side of the roomy attic, close enough for comfortable conversation after having retired.

The cat also found it an admirable place for the education of her numerous progeny in the way of learning the habits of venturesome roaches and unwary mice, and their nightly scampering after imaginary victims was another source of annoyance to the intolerant George who understood boisterousness in no one but himself.

One night, while disporting himself in playful, voluble mood and feeling that he was being interrupted too insistently by the chirping crickets and complaining katydids, he began abusing them and calling out to them after the manner of an irate parent trying to correct a heedless child. His expletives were magnificently humorous though delivered in all seriousness and intended to quell the innocent marauders of his peace. After patient waiting and earnest endeavor to carry on his conversation above their quiet din, he resorted to throwing his shoes and odd pieces of clothing and rolling bottles along the floor in the direction where he thought his tantalizing intruders might be, hoping to silence them with noisy missiles. The sight of rolling bottles in the moonlight was a pleasant invitation to the cat and kittens to join in the chase, and soon there was the joyous noise of a dozen pattering feet adding force to his increasing irritation. Again and again he tried his futile wiles to silence the annoying serenaders and romping kittens, but the happy little insects sang on unperturbed and the kittens continued to roll the bottles in dark corners at a safe distance. Realizing that he got no aid from me other than the undisguised appreciation of the delightful comedy, shown by my hearty laughter, he arranged himself on the side of his cot and began singing almost defiantly the gruesome spiritual called "Dry Bones," patting the time with his feet on the floor with such vehemence that it was not long before he was interrupted by a vision of "Miss Ellen," in her nightgown with a lighted candle in her hand, calling from the head of the stairs and asking quietly if he had no regard for the peace and quiet of the members of the household below stairs.

The crickets and katydids continued to sing, and realizing that he had been worsted, he sullenly wrapped his head in a towel and said he was going to try and pray.

DRY BONES

Piano

Down in de val-ley de sper-ret, spoke, 'Ze-kul, go proph-e-sy An' 'Ze-kul saw de val-ly full o'

(Verses 2,3,4)

Sper - ret tol' 'Ze-kul call de foa'winds foath An' breathe on de bones all slain— Be - hol' he heard a noise, ev - 'vy bone to his bone Come to - geth - uh an' lived a - gain De graves all op - ened an' de bones took breath an' de skin cov - ud o - vuh a - gain———— An' dey stood on dey feet like de ah - my o' my Lawd, O de bones— was liv - in' men— Some dem bones is my moth - uh's bones Come to - geth uh fo' to rise an shine— Some dem bones is my fath - uh's bones an' some o' dem bones is mine.—

(Chorus) Dry bones, etc.

V

Some dem bones is my sistuh's bones,
    Come togethuh fo' to rise and shine;
Some dem bones is my brethuh's bones,
    An' some o' dem bones is mine.

VI

Some dem bones goin'-a make me laugh
    Wen dey gathuh fo' to rise an' shine;
An, some dem bones goin'-a make me weep,
    'Cause some o' dem bones is mine.

GO DOWN, DEATH

OLD Uncle Andrew Barkis was not wholly dependent on wood-sawing for his support. Aunt Fanny Anderson gave him a room in her back yard, where he lived comfortably with George, his grandson, who brought him food every evening from "Miss Ellen's kitchen."

Presumably as far back as the early '30's, Uncle Andrew had been brought over a young man from the Guinea Coast and sold into Virginia, where he worked as a slave on the tobacco plantations. Several years before the Civil War, according to his own calculation, he was bought by the owner of the Labarre plantation, which was situated a short distance above the town of Gretna, just across the river from New Orleans, where he worked in the cane fields until Freedom was declared. He was very old at the time I knew him as a wood-sawyer and was beginning to get so infirm that he was scarcely able to go about without the help of his trusty broom-handle walking-stick and the watchful assistance of George, his devoted companion.

Uncle Andrew's appearance was strangely out of keeping with his simple, humble nature. His presence was most uninviting, a sort of cave-man African type, inspiring something like fear in little children who saw him for the first time. He retained several ancestral traits which filled the admiring George with boyish awe and envy; one of them being the occasional filing of his teeth to "keep 'um on aidge."

His life was one of unmistakable Christian devotion, and he was looked upon as a prop of the Little Rock Baptist Church, of which he was a long time member. But he seemed never to have been able to lose his fear and respect for some of his earlier African deities. Chief among them was one he called Pohn-ki-yea; one he frequently referred to and held up to George's impressionable mind as a person capable of performing terrible and mighty things. To be told that "Pohn-ki-yea watchin' an' gwine git yo' soul an' body ef yuh do wrong," was sufficient warning to make George a marvel of perfect deportment for three days hand-running.

Uncle Andrew's belief in witches was another ancestral inheritance. If he saw red marks on one's face in the morning, such as one sometimes has after a long, heavy sleep, usually on the cheek, often caused by wrinkles in the pillow, he would advance the strangest notions about witches having ridden you during the night. The red marks on your face were the marks of their bridles. "Witch bridles" was a fact you dared not question or dispute. The witches came about midnight and ran their bridles through your nostrils, then jumped on you and straddled your chest and drove you for a ride far out over the world. Snoring, breathing through your mouth and all other queer noises you made while asleep were due to the witches' bridles closing the nasal passages. If you were fortunate enough to awake before sunrise, and the window or door of your room happened to be open, then the witches could fly away before you had time to see them. But if the room happened to be well closed, then the witches could not get out and you were sure to see them. The only way you would be able to catch them would be to sprinkle mustard seeds across the doorway, and the witches would be obliged to pick them all up before sunrise; otherwise they were powerless and you could do with them as you pleased. They were great tricksters and very frequently resorted to the cunningest wiles to have you open the window or door while they were gathering up the mustard seeds, begging and pleading for more light and air to enable them to see better and breathe more freely in their hurry to accomplish their task before the sunlight came; imploring you to open the door and see if the sun was at all visible,—which, if you did, they would fly out instantly, and most certainly would come back that night to torment you with increased vigor for having tried to detain them. This fancy was so real to Uncle Andrew, and his descriptions of the witches were so fascinatingly minute that you found yourself believing in their existence almost as firmly as he did.

On Sundays Uncle Andrew was a person of importance and possession, and his derby hat and long-tail coat and stiff-bosom shirt, all bequeathed to him by various "w'ite-folks" for whom he sawed wood, were the admiration of all his neighbors as he went by on his way to church.

Uncle Andrew's voice was a husky, unsteady bass; and while you were scarcely impressed by his singing, you marveled at the strange barbaric songs he knew and wondered why you never heard anybody else sing them, and if they were ancestral memories of his native land, perhaps modified and fashioned to express the calmer emotion of the comforting religion learned in the new continent.

"Go Down, Death" is a dirge sung at wakes and funeral ceremonies. It is a sort of vocal dead march which seems to have been created to be sung at night, out under the open sky and the waning moon, to be borne away on the autumn wind to sigh over the graves of long-forgotten pilgrims of peace throughout the ages. The tone of triumphal command in the refrain, the thrilling iciness of fear conveyed in the unexpected C natural of the first bar of the refrain, the admirable consistency in sound and thought throughout, make it comparable to any of the classic death-songs of the primitive peoples whose music has come down to us.

Many years after I had taken down the melody from Uncle Andrew's singing, I tried to find out from the colored people of my village how many there were who knew the chant or remembered having heard it sung by the older generation; and invariably I was answered with, "Lawd, chile, da's ainshun days." One man only was able to give me a few verses of the hymn, which were very close to the version of Uncle Andrew. He procured them from Ma Ellen Shedrick, a very old woman who was known as the "Death Angel." She was always called upon to sing at the deathbed of a sinner in order to make easy the passage over hell-fire. Together with the verses sung by Uncle Andrew and the ones procured from the "Death Angel," I was enabled to construct what appears to be a consecutive picture of a soul's departing, told with a graphic cruelty reflecting a savage poetry bordering on the sublime.

GO DOWN, DEATH

ea - sy, An' — bring my · ser - van' home.

(Verse 7)

Maach up in de king - dom ea - sy, I want yuh

maach up in de king - dom ea - sy, I want yuh maach up in de king - dom

ea - sy, An' — bring my ser - van' home.

III

Close up de eyelids easy,

I want yuh close up de eyelids easy,

I want yuh close up de eyelids easy,

An' bring my servan' home.

IV

Cut loose de heaht-strings easy,

I want yuh cut loose de heaht-strings easy,

I want yuh cut loose de heaht-strings easy,

An' bring my servan' home.

V

Step to de graveyahd easy,

I want yuh step to de graveyahd easy,

I want yuh step to de graveyahd easy,

An' bring my servan' home.

VI

Pass ovuh Hell-flame easy,

I want yuh pass ovuh Hell-flame easy,

I want yuh pass ovuh Hell-flame easy,

An' bring my servan' home.

I'M GOIN' HOME ON A CLOUD

OLD Aunt Fanny was the obedient wife of King Murphy; both having been slaves on the Derbigny plantation just above the town of Gretna. King had only one arm, was slightly lame and walked with the aid of an old umbrella stick. Aunt Fanny's dynasty will be best remembered for her long and efficient reign as queen of the kitchen at Mme. Jacquin's fashionable Creole boarding-house for itinerant school teachers and court house officials, during which time she was enabled to bestow upon her regal spouse the befitting attention and full tribute demanded of a faithful subject.

There was nothing of the plebeian about King; the travail and tedium of everyday life were things of which he made little reckoning. Once in a while he seemed to feel a desire to break the monotony of things and would respond to the pastoral urge of setting out lettuce plants in the truck garden "up the coast," provided the weather was fair and Mr. Peters happened to be short of help and offered good pay in consequence.

King was a familiar figure every Saturday evening, when he appeared in his stiff-starched blue cottonade jumper, pounding with his umbrella stick on Mme. Jacquin's back gate for Fanny to come out and deliver the weekly stipend before she had time to indulge too freely in her favorite mixture of gin and raspberry syrup at Mr. Cardeilhac's barroom just across the street.

After King's death Aunt Fanny's twilight lamentations were loud and lugubrious, and she drank magnificently to his imperious memory.   She occupied an upstairs room over the Jacquin cow-stable, and passers-by enjoyed many a nightly performance listening to her plaintive intoning of the numerous virtues of the departed King and her singing of wistful spirituals like "I'm Goin' Home on a Cloud."

I'M GOIN' HOME ON A CLOUD

One dese fine maw-nin's at break of day, I'm go-in'
home on a cloud.—— King Death gwine fin' me hyeah at my
play, I'm go-in' ho-me on— a cloud.

WHO'S GOIN' TO CLOSE MY DYIN' EYES?

PICTURE in your mind a cool, moonlight night in early autumn. You are sitting out on the front veranda of an old plantation house, looking across the garden, watching the lightning-bugs darting in and out among the jasmine bushes, and listening to the mockingbirds singing in the cedar trees.

Suddenly you are aware of a snatch of plaintive melody going over you on the breeze. You listen, and you catch the far-away sound of voices singing in the distance. The breeze goes by again, carrying with it the sound of sorrow and the burden of mourning. You know then that some colored person is dead in one of the quarters just across the field, and that the night watch has begun and all the church members and friends and neighbors from the village far and near are gathered there in the room, sitting around in rows, chanting dirge-like prayer songs and singing the departed spirit down the undiscovered road where childish faith leads them on unquestioning.

You are moved by the archaic solemnity of the occasion and feel impelled to become an intimate witness; so you follow the wake of the mournful music, across the dew-drenched field of camomile flowers glimmering in the moonlight like a fantastic winding-sheet,— beyond the picket fence and the gloomy

clump of thorn trees by the pond, until you come to the right house at last, guided by the thin ribbon of lamplight falling along the narrow footpath.

How long you stood by the window listening outside in the moonlight, pondering over the drama of mysterious departure, you will never recall; for under the spell of enchantment such as this, reason becomes nebulous and remembrance gives way to dreams of bewilderment. But you know afterward in the full light of awakened consciousness that your

"Head got wet wid de midnight dew;
De mawnin' star was a witness, too."

Such was my experience the first night I heard the singing of "Who's Goin' to Close My Dyin' Eyes." The complete number of stanzas were given to me afterward by Rebecca Hutton.

WHO'S GOIN' TO CLOSE MY DYIN' EYES?

O I don' wan' be bur-ied in de stawm, O Law-dy, I don' wan' be bur-ied in de stawm. O An-gel, O An-gel, I don' wan' be bur-ied in de stawm.

69

IV

Dig my grave wid a golden spade,
     O Lawdy,
Dig my grave wid a golden spade,
     O angel, O angel,
Dig my grave wid a golden spade.

V

Low' me down wid a silvuh chain,
     O Lawdy,
Low' me down wid a silvuh chain,
     O angel, O angel,
Low me down wid a silvuh chain.

VI

Windin' sheet goin' hol' me fas',
     O Lawdy,
Windin' sheet goin' hol' me fas',
     O angel, O angel,
Windin' sheet goin' hol' me fas'.

VII

Coffin lid goin' screw me down,
     O Lawdy,
Coffin lid goin' screw me down,
     O angel, O angel,
Coffin lid goin' screw me down.

VIII

Good-by, my voice be heard no mo',
     O Lawdy,
Good-by, my voice be heard no mo',
     O angel, O angel,
Good-by, my voice be heard no mo'.

O MARY, WHERE IS YOUR BABY?

IF it happened to be a moonlight night in summer, then the back gallery of the "big house" was a most favorable resort for melancholy song revels and wistful meditations; for it was there Cornelius Williams would be entertained when he came to woo Betty Winston, the cook.

Either from a strange sense of timidity which Betty possessed or her love of sociability, she was never alone with Cornelius on these moonlight rendezvous. This was a fortunate thing in the cause of music; for George, Simon, Daniel, Martha and Jessie, who usually acted as chorus, all had splendid voices; and with Betty and Cornelius as soloists, the ensemble was nothing short of ravishing.

A generous pitcher of lemonade always added zest to the conviviality of these meetings, which lasted late into the night,—until "Miss Ellen had her first sleep," at which time she would knock gently but positively to remind Betty and her harmonious adherents that it was the hour for all festivities to end.

"O Mary, Where is Your Baby" was a great favorite with Betty and her able chorus, and their fervent singing of its poignant refrain was something memorable. It seems to have fixed itself in my memory as a sort of dream-song chanted by voices in the distance,—gentle voices singing querulously in the moonlight.

The song was evolved by a colored missionary called Sister Mackey, a woman of unusual native talent. The melody is strongly reminiscent of the ante-bellum "Swing Low, Sweet Chariot," but the noble refrain after each verse has a ring of true originality, and the quaint flavor of the words is most interesting.

Several of Sister Mackey's spirituals were sung for the first time at Putney Ward's church in the town of Gretna, and they became general favorites in all the colored churches very soon afterward.

O MARY, WHERE IS YOUR BABY?

man - juh An' cah'y'd him to de th'one.

Read a - bout de eld - uhs an' de He - brew pries' A -

preach - in' in de tab - ba - nick - ul hall

Stan - in' in a won - duh at de words dey heard Fum a

li'l boy chile so small. O li'l boy, how ole you is. —

Tell it if yuh let it be —— tol', O

li'l boy, how ole yuh is, I ain' but twelve yeahs ole.

POOR LITTLE JESUS

MATHILDE was the wife of Burl Hardy, sometimes preacher at the Evening Star Baptist Church, sometimes saw-filer at the Union Stave Factory which was "close by Sis' Susan Smiley cook-shop." Burl and Mathilde lived across the yard in the old building which served as the servants' quarters of the Toledano family during their régime on the plantation. Mathilde was cook at the "big house," and her "vagrant utterances, swinging soft in the music of the moment," were not confined to the kitchen but happily floated into the dining-room and helped to beguile many a wholesome meal.

She always sang best, however, when Burl was present; so whenever we wanted an evening of extraordinary entertainment for any city friends we planned a program beginning with an impromptu sermon by Burl, followed by the singing of spirituals by Mathilde, assisted by Liney, Toofay, Phonsie and Burl; ending with climactic dances such as the "catch-scratch," the "buzzard-lope" and the "Cincinnati Pas," performed by Liney and Toofay. This last named dance they always referred to as "Sistuh Natty."

A program of this kind was arranged for the entertainment of a group of friends one Sunday night in the large dining-room. Mathilde had decorated all the windows and doors of the room with long, trailing festoons of honeysuckle intertwined with moss roses and deadly night-shade; and in odd corners of the room had placed large Creole water jars with great clusters of royal purple thistles she had gathered at sun-down with the drowsy honey-laden bumble bees still clinging to them,

—unconsciously giving expression to the meaningful sense of the natural affinity between man and Nature and the poetic impulse of the primitive heart.

Burl was asked to be somewhat gentle in his defense of Christianity and its ardent supporters because several Jewish friends would be among those present. He promised that he would "talk no random," and asked if he might wear his long black overcoat, an antiquated, ministerial-looking garment of German make, given to him by a member of the family after it had done long service. Although the coat was not reasonably consistent with the hot August weather, he was given permission to wear it; and when asked his reason for wanting to do so, he said: "Well, wen I puts on dis coat I feels equal to inny assawtment."

Burl's sermon that night was about "John de Revalatuh: done it in a minute," which he said he took from "de one-eye chaptuh o' de two-eye John," and it was a masterpiece of inspired rhetoric, interpretative reading and astounding information.

Mathilde's important contribution was the classic, "Po' Li'l Jesus." The general mold of the melody is so reminiscent of the Gregorian chant that it may not be unreasonable to assume it is due to the influence of Roman Catholicism, the religion of Creole Louisiana, and the religion adopted by many of the Negroes of the Creole plantations. Many of them who belonged to Catholic owners have professed that belief and have also been members of the Baptist church, thereby bringing about a strange and interesting expression of faith.

PO' LI'L JESUS

Tuck 'im fum a man-juh, Hail Lawd, Tuck 'im fum 'is moth-uh,

Hail Lawd, Ain' dat a pi-ty an' a shame.——

III
Po' li'l Jesus,
   Hail Lawd,
Dey gi'n 'im to de Hebrew,
   Hail Lawd,
Dey spit on 'is gahment,
   Hail Lawd,
Ain' dat a pity an' a shame?

IV
Po' li'l Jesus,
   Hail Lawd,
Dey boun' 'im wid a haltuh,
   Hail Lawd,
Whupped 'im up de mountain,
   Hail Lawd,
Ain' dat a pity an' a shame?

V
Po' li'l Jesus,
   Hail Lawd,
Dey nailed 'im to de cross,
   Hail Lawd,
Dey hung 'im wid de robbuh,
   Hail Lawd,
Ain' dat a pity an' a shame?

VI
Po' li'l Jesus,
   Hail Lawd,
Risen fum de dahkness,
   Hail Lawd,
'Scended into glory,
   Hail Lawd,
Ain' dat a pity an' a shame?

VII
Po' li'l Jesus,
   Hail Lawd,
Meet me in de kingdom,
   Hail Lawd,
Lead me to my Fathuh,
   Hail Lawd,
Ain' dat a pity an' a shame?

TROUBLES WAS HARD

EVERYBODY in the village knew old Uncle Ned Wineberry and respected him for his honesty and upright dealing. He had two mules and two dump carts and supported himself and his daughter Hannah by chopping firewood and selling it in cord lengths to the townspeople. All the children of the village loved him because he would let them ride in his dump cart whenever he came along without a load of wood, and Uncle Ned and his old mule Doaner and a cart full of merry laughing children, both white and colored, was a picture familiar to every neighborhood.

He was a most respectable old man and his disapproval of drinking and loose conduct of any kind was the topic of discussion among many of his critical and more tolerant church members.

One Sunday morning Uncle Ned was on his way home after delivering a load of wood, when he heard somebody call him. He checked his mule and stopped, and looking around he saw Phillis, one of his church members, coming up in the middle of the dusty street to talk to him.

Cora, a young colored woman who was notorious for drinking and wandering away from home and taking shelter anywhere she chanced to stumble, had found her way to Phillis's house and was sitting on the front steps "drunk as uncawnshubble cattul," as Phillis expressed it with biting contempt. She asked Uncle Ned if he would drive around and put Cora in his cart and take her home. Uncle Ned demurred and expressed his embarrassment at being seen with a drunken woman in his cart by all the "w'ite-folks" on their way home from Sunday morning service, but Phillis prevailed on his charity until he consented to assist her.

Together they picked up the oblivious Cora and carried her from the steps and placed her on the floor of the dump cart in a sitting position, then Uncle Ned started up the street on a jog trot with his unwelcome burden. The motion of the jolting cart continued to move the unresisting Cora little by little toward the end, and as Uncle Ned had neglected to put the tailboard in place, it was not long before the unfortunate Cora was jolted out of the cart and lay prostrate in the dust, staring into eternity. Uncle Ned turned around, and seeing his unworthy burden gone, gave a flip of the reins to his mule, and exclaiming, "Dah, bless Gawd!—Git up, Doanuh,"—he straightway began singing "His Troubles Was Hard" and drove on reckless of Cora's fate.

The complete number of verses I got from Hattie Sparks some time afterward.

TROUBLES WAS HARD

Tell yuh 'bout a man wat live be-fo' Chris'— His name was A-dam, Eve was his wife.

Tell yuh how dat man he lead a rug-ged life, All be-cause he tak-en de 'oo-man's ad-vice,— She made his

trou-ble so hard,———   She made his trou-ble so hard,———

Lawd, Lawd, she made his   trou-ble so hard.———

Yas   in   deed———   his   trou-ble was hard.———

(2nd & 3rd Verse)
Now lem-me tell you wat Da-vid done, Ole man Jes-se

young es' son, He slew'd Go-li-ah de might-y one, An'

Saul puh-sued him an' he had to run, An' his

IV

Now all my membuhs settin' hyeah on yo' seat,
Got somethin' to tell yuh so shawt an' sweet,—
W'en all Gawd's people in glory meet
Dey gwine slip an' slide on Gawd's golden street.
'Cause dey troubles was hahd,
Yas dey troubles was hahd, Lawd, Lawd;
O dey troubles was hahd,
Yas indeed, dey troubles was hahd.

I GOT A HOME IN THE ROCK

TO be able to sing any time or all the time seemed to be the chief aim of Hattie Sparks' life. She had the sunniest disposition of any colored person I ever knew; and throughout the twenty-odd years of her faithful service in my sister's household I can only think of her laughing or singing. The children loved her as much as she loved them, and the way she bossed them and commanded them in one breath and laughed and sang to them in the next was one of the happy charms of having her about.

Whether she was down on her knees scrubbing the kitchen floor, or standing over the washtub rubbing strenuously, or hovering over the cook stove deep in the fragrant mysteries of a jambalaya of rice and chorisse and tomatoes or the intricacies of a crab gumbo, or bending over the ironing-board out in the yard under the sycamore tree where a fitful breeze fanned her now and then, her heart was always full of song and her voice was a resounding horn.

Hattie's mother died when she was a small child and she was brought up by her stepmother, Eliza Ward, who was considered "big folks" and "high-up people" by the colored residents of the East Green; not because she was the daughter of Putney Ward, the eloquent elder of the New Hope Baptist Church, but because she was a graduate of the Southern University, the leading colored college of New Orleans, and because she played the piano. The influence of this pleasant environment must surely have accounted for Hattie's real ability as a domestic, likewise for her love of song and her extensive knowledge of hymns and spirituals old and new. She furnished me with a great many of them, often writing out the words, supplying variants when it was possible, and, as in the case of "I Got a Home in the Rock," furnishing a totally different set of words sung to the same tune, called,

AIN'T IT GRAND

I got a letter from my Father in my hand,
Written by my elder brother and it's grand;
   It was written o'er the sea
   And was forward unto me,
And I'm happy as can be in this land.

My Father told me in His letter things was grand;
That I could make myself no better in this land.
   I cried, Lord what shall I do?
   For I had not read it through,
And it made me all anew in this land.

Now I am a new creation in this land,
I am free from condemnation, ain't that grand?
   I can shout and sing and play,
   And I'm happy all the day,
And my soul can hardly stay in this land.

I'm a stranger to this nation in this land;
They don't know my situation, but it's grand.
   I got wealth that can't be told,—
   My Father's riches to behold,
And my kindred never grow old in this land.

Now I'm not afraid of dying in this land;
I can shout at Jesus' coming, ain't that grand?
  All this world is dark as night,
  But my Father's face is bright,
And I'm walking in the light in this land.

Death he is a cruel monster in this land;
You can call but he won't answer, ain't it grand?
  I can leave at break of day,
  You will find but empty clay,—
Lord, I wonder what they'll say when I'm gone?

There is an unusual sophistication here which raises this hymn to a higher place in the poetic scale than many of them attain. There is a feeling of happiness and grateful trust and resignation of real beauty. The varying emotions of the last stanza are wonderfully expressive of the visionary, heaven-seeking, world-loving, inquisitive Negro mind. The only difference in singing these words to the melody of "I Got a Home in the Rock" is, the last three words of the first, second and fifth lines of each stanza are not repeated as they are in "I Got a Home in the Rock."

I GOT A HOME IN THE ROCK

Piano

I got a home in de rock don't yuh see, don't yuh see; I got a home in de rock don't yuh see. 'Tis half way be-tween de hea-ven an' de earth I

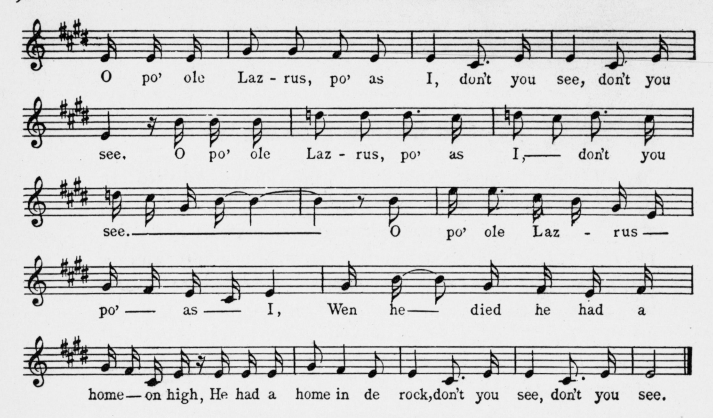

O po' ole Laz-rus, po' as I, don't you see, don't you see, O po' ole Laz-rus, po' as I,— don't you see.— O po' ole Laz-rus— po'— as— I, Wen he— died he had a home—on high, He had a home in de rock, don't you see, don't you see.

IV

Ole man Paul he lived in Rome, lived in Rome,
Ole man Paul he lived in Rome;
    Ole man Paul he lived in Rome,
    But yondah in Tawshuh was his home,
He had a home in de rock, don't you see, don't you see.

V

O rock of ages clef' fo' me, clef' fo' me,
O rock of ages clef' fo' me;
    O rock of ages clef' fo' me,
    O let-a me hide-a myself in thee,
I got a home in de rock, don't you see, don't you see.

VI

O mothuh, mothuh, don't you cry, don't you cry,
O mothuh, O mothuh, don't you cry;
    O mothuh, mothuh, don't you cry,
    Wid de faith I got I'm goin' to die,
I got a home in de rock, don't you see, don't you see.

VII

Gawd give Noah de rainbow sign, rainbow sign,
Gawd give Noah de rainbow sign;
    Gawd give Noah de rainbow sign,
    He tol' him no mo' watuh but fiah nex' time,—
O get a home in de rock, don't you see, don't you see.

O LORD, HOW LONG?

NO more accurate record of the Negro's life can be desired than the rhythmic, poetic, melodious one portrayed so faithfully in his songs. They seem to have gathered together all the simple, most unforgettable thoughts of the generation, infused with the rural, free, out-of-door charm lending them a sort of witchery that is irresistible. Their very artlessness helps to make them a perfection of art. The verses of some of them might be likened to "true poetry written only to one's own heart to record the pain or joy, like a soul's diary whose sweetness can be kept when it is hidden secretly, or like a real prayer for which only a few words uttered are enough."

A splendid example is "O Lord, How Long?" which might be the crooning of an old man in one of his scriptural moods. You seem to see him sitting in the shade of a persimmon tree, early in the morning, the fragrant blossoms dropping down upon the ground all about him. He has a loose bundle of willow saplings spread out in front of him, which he is cutting into long narrow swathes to be woven into baskets to be sold to the *marchande* women for carrying vegetables on their heads. As he works he is thinking of the many years he has seen pass over him, the long privations he has endured, and the unprepared condition of his soul if he were called

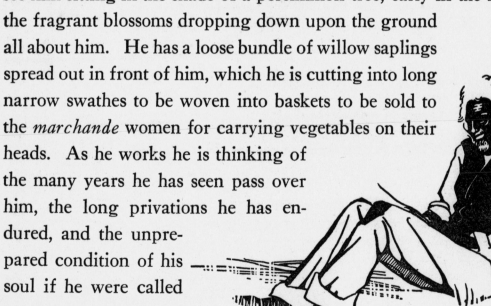

away suddenly to meet his Creator, and the futility of life in general. Gradually his thought takes the form of verse, and intuitively he begins to improvise a melody faithfully recording the wistful burden of his soul.

This spiritual was a special favorite with George Riley, and whenever its plaintive echoes went murmuring through the house more than once during the evening, you were then certain that it was George's sacrament week and it was a signal for you to help him "fight the devil" in order that he might overcome.

O LORD, HOW LONG?

LONESOME VALLEY

OF all simple, trusting, God-fearing people, George Riley took his religion with more seriousness than anybody I ever knew, whether white or colored. Singing and praying, according to his belief, were the only legitimate services ordained to move and stir people to the sweetness of the word of God; and their singing and praying had to be confined to psalms and hymns and sober, discreet and devout music. Merry tunes and capricious airs were whisperings of the devil, and anyone who delighted in them was lost irrevocably. If he had possessed the fortunate gift of letters, how thankfully he would have revelled in reading of those quaint old monks and reformers of the reign of Henry VIII and their laughable attempts to put down the flourishing growth of songs and ballads of the Minstrels of that time. I can imagine his glowing pleasure on reading good old Bishop Miles Coverdale's "Address to the Christian," written in 1538:

"Wolde to God that our Mynstrels had none other thynge to play on, neither our carters and plowmen other thynge to whistle upon, save psalmes, hymns, and such like godly songes. If women at the rockes [distaffs] and spinnynge at the wheles, had none other songes to pass their tyme withal than such as Moses' sister songe before them, they should be better occupied than with 'Hey, nonny, nonny; Hey, trolly, lolly', and such fantasies."

George always sang at his work, but his songs were the traditional spirituals of his race, never the secular melodies adapted to sacred use by the Methodists, Presbyterians and Salvationists; the kind which the austere old friar Erasmus must have had in mind when he made the following pronouncement: "We have brought a tedious and capricious kind of music into the house of God, a tumultuous noise of different voices, such as I think was never heard in the theatres either of the Greeks or the Romans."

Unconsciously George's motto must have been, "one single groan in the spirit is worth the diapason of all the church music in the world." And if it happened to be his "saccament week," his groans were epochal. This sacrament week came once a month, and beginning on Monday it was a week of introspection and examination of conscience and prayer-chanting that compelled your respect because of its childish, unfeigned sincerity. It also caused you to experience a certain feeling of repression, because you knew you must not laugh with any freedom or indulge in any phase of respectable merriment or light conversation or joyous music or song if you wanted to escape being told with scornful vehemence that "nothin' but de Devil sont yuh hyeah fo' a tawment, 'cause yuh knows dis my saccament week an' I'm pray'n."

Duties were performed with patience and precision, every want was attended to conscientiously, questions were answered and domestic civilities were without change; but you were expected to remember that you must not become an obstacle in the path of the servant of the Lord. After Sunday and sacrament-taking George was a different person. The house was happier because his groans of spirit forsook the minor mood and flowed out in major melody.

George always entertained his visitors in the kitchen. Perhaps for the important reason that the ice-box was near at hand, permitting him to dispense the "left-overs" with imposing hospitality,—a thing to his mind, the chief requisite and virtue of a Southern gentleman no matter how humble his station.

If the visitor happened to be a personable one such as Toatsie, his "link" and "water-brother," then the kitchen became a charmed place and the lure of music never failed to draw me down stairs and succeed in holding me a captive listener.

Toatsie's right name was Joseph François. He was a deacon as well as a member of George's church, and his repertoire of hymns was unlimited. His voice was a deep, pleasing baritone, and his singing of "The Blind Man Stood on the Road and Cried" would move the most obdurate listener to tears.

LONESOME VALLEY

val - ley,— Go down in de lone-some val - ley, my Lawd, Go
down in de lone-some val - ley, To meet my Sav-iuh there.

2nd Verse

Want to en - tuh yon-dah in de king'-dom, Go down in de
lone-some val - ley, Whah my fat - huh is buil-din me a man-shun,
Go down in de lone-some val - ley, Go down in de lone -some
val - ley, Go down in de lone-some val - ley, my Lawd, Go
down in de lone -some val - ley, To meet my Sa - viuh there.

III

Want to gathuh at de welcome table?
  Go down in de lonesome valley.
Want to feed on flowin' milk an' honey?
  Go down in de lonesome valley.

(Chorus)

Go down in de lonesome valley,
Go down in de lonesome valley, my Lawd,
Go down in de lonesome valley,
  To meet my Saviuh there.

THE BLIND MAN STOOD ON THE ROAD AND CRIED

IT was easy to understand George Riley's boasted pride in the friend-ship existing between Toatsie and himself when you knew that they had entered the church ranks together, becoming "links," bound to each other in the symbolic chain of Christian fellowship; and that they were also "water-brothers," having gone down into the pool together as candidates for baptism; and that they were also fellow-members of the Golden Spray Lodge, Uniform Rank, "Knights o' Peefus."

Perhaps this last affiliation they enjoyed most of all, in that once a year they could disport themselves in the spectacular parade, with "jim-swinger coats" and plumed hats and badges and rosettes "swung 'cross de buzzum," with banners and spears and battle-axes and other cryptic regalia; with the crowd marching with them through the town to the seductive Pied-Piper music of the band that enticed the children from every quarter until the procession became an endless trail of light-step-ping, dancing merry-makers.

Another feature of the Lodge was the "settin'-up watches" whenever there was a sick member who required extra attention outside of his family. While these "settin'-up watches" may have lacked the pomp and excitement the parade offered, they made up for the deficiency in the way of sweet singing and good coffee and crackers and cheese, all helping materially to make the night hours pass pleasantly.

During the lingering illness of Brother William Henry, lodge member and church member as well, George and Toatsie had been called on several times to serve as watchers, and they were present the night of his death. Their dramatic account of Brother Henry's departure from life was a remarkable piece of narrative, and their consternation at the disclosure made by him was not soon forgotten. He was not a native of the place, having come to town many years before his death a stranger from Natchez, Mississippi; and becoming a member of the church he was soon looked upon with trust and respect by all. Therefore it is not surprising that the amazed congregation should be moved to have a printed record made of his death-bed confession from the recital of all who were present and heard it, using it as a warning to all unwary ones without the fold and the unrighteous ones likewise within.

As an emotional human document it is both curious and interesting. It was printed on a single sheet, the headlines in bold type, the spelling occasionally incorrect, with little or no punctuation; and it was sold at five cents a copy by the members of the congregation, the money going to help defray the expense of the funeral, which "was preached just as he lived, to let the world know."

Whether it is a sincere confession or nothing more than the religious ravings of a fever-troubled brain, it has a certain poetic quality and rhythmic flow resembling the rhapsodic visions of some of the minor prophets of the Bible; so I have taken the liberty of changing the crude prose form in which it is printed and have given the lines a sort of *vers libre* arrangement, the form such utterances naturally take. I have added the necessary punctuation but have left the spelling unchanged.

THE DYING TESTIMONY

of

BROTHER WILLIAM HENRY

Who served in the Church 32 years
and on the 11th day of February
he made his bed in Hell.

READ WHAT HE SAID JUST BEFORE DEATH CAME

"I have been a member of the church for 32 years,
I have drink Christ's blood
Also eaten his bread,
Also stood before the church
And told them that I was born of God.
But I was untrue;
Yes, I prayed for the sick and helped the poor;
I was counted by all to be the best prayer among men;
I could sing well that all men would praise me,
But I have made my bed in hell.

Look Out, Devel,
Your fork is too long and hot.
Pull up my quilt,—
That's so, you can't,
For it is too short to cover my feet,—

It is getting shorter and shorter.
Close the door,—
I can't stand the sight of Him who died for all.

Say, Willie, come here,
Don't let me fall too fast for my way is dark,
There is no light to shine upon the road.

Say, Walker, come here,—
Yonder is a man with his back turned to me,
It looks like the man I have been praying to for 32 years.
Call Him and ask Him to turn once more to me,
I have called Him but he won't answer me.
Oh! what a mistake I have made.
Hell is hot, hot, hot,
Too hot to stay always.

(Brother Charlie ask him did he want the pastor to pray
    for him)

No, no, no,—
I told him last Sunday that I was Heaven bound,
But I am hell bound.
Tell Revs. Hall, Williams, Judge and Paul
That I was the cause of they and their families suffering.
I made their road hard
And kept the members from church
To keep them on a drag.
How often have I broke up the preachers' plans
And offered to fight them,
But they was right and I was wrong.

Tell Sister Mary Jones to come here,
I want to tell her that the plot
She and I have made up to kill the preacher,—
I want to tell her to stop,
If not, she will go to hell
Just as I am going now.

The hell bound train is at my bedside,
Old Satan is the conductor.
All the prayers I have prayed,
Songs I have sung,
Have turned to flames of fire all around me.

Henry Thomas and Will have fought every preacher,—
Not only our preacher, but all,
And made them fail and go down.
Boys stop! boys stop that,—
If not, you will go to hell just as I am going now.
I am near hell's dark door.
Oh! how dark.
It is raining down Brimstone.
Hell is on fire,
My bed is burning up.
I have played too long,
The sun is almost down,
The lamps of life is almost out.
It's bad to play with God.

(Brother Walter began to sing "Jesus Can Make a Dying
    Bed Feel Soft as Downie Pillows Are")

Don't sing that,
For it makes my bed harder.
Put form and fashion aside,
If not, you will be lost.
Say, take that chain off me;
I can go to hell without you putting that chain on me.

Why should you chain me?
I have done your work well,
I have given your church trouble,
I have helped to kill preachers behind their backs
And laughed at them dying,
Now I am going to hell;
God's word proves it well.
The pits that I have dug for others
They have turned to a Gulf of despair for me to fall in.
I can't fool God."

Just as Brother Henry breathed his last breath, George and Toatsie began singing "The Blind Man Stood on the Road and Cried." In form this spiritual somewhat resembles the one called "I Got a Home in the Rock."

BLIND MAN STOOD ON THE ROAD AND CRIED

O de blin' man stood on de road—an' cried, road an' cried, O de blin' man stood on de road an' cried, road an' cried, Cry-in' O——— Law - dy

save me, O Law-dy, De blin' man

stood on de ro-ad an' cried.

II

Cryin' Lawd have mercy on my soul, on my soul,

Cryin' Lawd have mercy on my soul, on my soul:

Cryin' O Lawdy, save me, O Lawdy,

De blind man stood on de road an' cried.

III

I ain' been to heav'n but I been tol', I been tol',

O I ain' been to heav'n but I been tol', I been tol';

Cryin' O Lawdy, save me, O Lawdy,

De blind man stood on de road an' cried.

IV

O my Lawd goin'-a wash me w'ituh 'an snow, w'ituh 'an snow,

Yas my Lawd goin'-a wash me w'ituh 'an snow, w'ituh 'an snow;

Cryin' O Lawdy, save me, O Lawdy,

De blind man stood on de road an' cried.

I FOLD UP MY ARMS AND I WONDER

WHILE this noble melody has an element of sophistication not usual in Negro spirituals, it also has certain marked characteristics which point to native origin. The verses are borrowed from the Protestant hymnal, slightly altered and embellished with a chorus of touching simplicity most expressive of the "yearning plaintive music of earth's sadder minstrelsy."

The original words have an interesting history extending over a century and a half and emanating from a race far different and distant from the singing people who have adapted and glorified them to their religious needs. They were written in 1745 by the Rev. William Williams, a Welsh divine and prolific writer of sacred songs, whose religious literature did more than anything else to interest the people and create a taste for reading in many parts of Wales. In 1758 a volume containing about eight hundred of his hymns was published and became a general favorite. It is still in use in the Established Church and among the different denominations everywhere. The Welsh title of this hymn in question is "Arglwydd, arwain trwy'r anialwch" ("Guide Me O Thou Great Jehovah)," and was translated into English by Peter Williams in 1772. It has undergone several alterations by various hands, which accounts for the frequent uncertainty as to authorship. In the Salisbury Hymn Book edited by Earl Nelson (1857), it is complete in four stanzas and they are attributed to John Keble. In another collection of the same year there are four stanzas ascribed to John B. Dykes, reading as follows:

Guide me O Thou great Jehovah,
   Pilgrim through this barren land;
I am weak, but Thou art mighty;
   Hold me with Thy powerful hand.

Open now the crystal fountains
   Whence the living waters flow;
Let the fiery, cloudy pillar
   Lead me all my journey through.

Feed me with the heavenly manna
   In this barren wilderness;
Be my sword, and shield, and banner,
   Be the Lord my Righteousness.

When I tread the verge of Jordan,
   Bid my anxious fears subside;
Death of death, and hell's destruction,
   Land me safe on Canaan's side.

In another collection of hymns published in 1863, it is attributed to Edward J. Hopkins and only three stanzas are given; the second line of the second stanza reading:

"Whence the healing streams do flow."

The stanza, "Feed me with the heavenly manna," is not given at all. The stanza, "Bread of heaven, bread of heaven," given in the Negro version of the hymn seems to recall the words of the old hymn sung at the communion service in the Methodist and the Episcopal churches. In an old book called the "Star of the East" by J. Conder, published in

1824, there is a hymn as follows: "For the eucharist—'I am the living bread which came down from heaven. . . . Whoso eateth my flesh, and drinketh my blood, hath eternal life. . . . I am the true vine.'"

—John VI, 51-4, XV, 1.

"Bread of heaven! on thee I feed,
    For thy flesh is meat indeed.
    Ever may my soul be fed
    With this true and living bread;
    Day by day with strength supplied,
    Through the life of Him who died."

It may be found also, with slight variations, in the following hymn books: Conder's Congregational Hymn Book, 1836; Cook & Denton Hymnal, 1853; Baptist Psalms and Hymns, 1858. In the Mitre Hymn Book, 1836, the opening line is altered to,

"Bread of life in mercy broken."

It is reasonable to look upon these early versions as the direct ancestors of the Negro offspring, accepting the Welsh translation of "Guide Me O Thou Great Jehovah" as the honorable first-parent of "I Fold Up My Arms and I Wonder." But there is certainly no discoverable relationship between the Negro melody and any of the melodies given in the above mentioned books, each being different and vastly inferior to the expressive Negro one.

It was sung to me by Emma Roussell, who was a Baptist and had never attended a service at any church but her own. She said it was an old "ballet" she learned from her mother, who had been a slave on the Destrehan plantation.

I FOLD UP MY ARMS AND I WONDER

Piano

Guide me, O thou great Je - ho - vah—

Pil - grim thro' this bar - ren lan'.— I am weak but thou art

might - y— Hol' me in Thy pow'r - ful han' O I

fold up my arms an' I won - der, O Lawd I won - der, Good Lawd I

won der___ Yes I fold up my arms an' I

won-der___ How far I'm a-way from my home.———

II

Open now the crystal fountain,
  Whence the healing watuhs flow;
Let the fiery, cloudy pilluh
  Lead me all my journey through.

(Chorus)

  O I fold up my arms an' I wonduh,
  O Lawd I wonduh, good Lawd I wonduh;
  Yes I fold up my arms an' I wonduh
  How far I'm away from my home.

III

Wen I tread the verge o' Jurden,
  Bid my anxious fear subside;
Lead me through the swelling currents,
  Land me safe on Cayn'yun's side.

(Chorus) O I fold up my arms, etc.

IV

Bread of heav'n, bread of heav'n,
  Feed me till I want no mo';
Be my strength, my strong deliv'ruh,
  Guide me to my Fathuh's sho'.

(Chorus) O I fold up my arms, etc.

IF YOU CAN'T COME, SEND ONE ANGEL DOWN

THE singer of this entrancing spiritual, known as a "shout," was "Doctuh Giles, brethuh de seven sons, Montanyul hawse trainuh an' king o' coons,"—to give his full pedigree as he declaimed it with sonorous tone and lofty eloquence. The "Montanyul" was his word for Montana; and if the horse he drove was one of that breed it must surely have been trained during the earliest history of that pioneer region, if appearance denoted anything.

Dr. Giles was a trader in horses, cows, goats, saddles and bridles, Creole chickens, guinea fowls, wheelbarrows, coon skins, yam potatoes, and any object inanimate or otherwise, on which he could realize a small profit. He made periodical visits to town in his rickety jumper which was hardly large enough to accommodate his lanky figure, nevertheless would have stowed within its limited space between the seat and the foot-rest, a small pig, or a bundle of malodorous coon-skins, or a sack full of jaw-bones of cattle which he would exchange at the ragman's emporium for a "jimmyjohn" to hold molasses or for some old rags "to make smoke wid."

Dr. Giles had a long, black mustache, and he wore a large felt sombrero with squirrel tails hanging all around the band, and the crown decorated with an assortment of small tin tags that are found on the various brands of chewing tobacco. He would drive up in front of a barroom or a grocery store, and in a stentorian voice would announce himself, always giving his full pedigree, then proclaim his merchandise and its unique worth, in this way attracting a crowd of curious idlers and admiring listeners.

His jaded old horse was always at the disposal of any prospective buyer, and upon receiving a bid he would recount a list of its remarkable traits, beside which the records of the steed of Mazeppa, the renowned Rosinante, and the classical Pegasus were but shimmering trifles.

Dr. Giles also enjoyed something of a reputation as a "hoodoo" doctor. His power to remove spells and cure any "ling'rin' mizry" was recognized by all the colored people of the coast "fum Taah-bone to Tuccapaw" (Terrebonne to Attacapas, parishes in southern Louisiana). His cure for rheumatism was infallible. It was a simple formula: ground worms which must be dug up before sunrise, fried in hog lard with parsley and Cayenne pepper; to be applied to the affected part, with hard rubbing in a downward direction, because "de mizry had to pass out thoo de toes." His cure for fever had something of a poetic flavor about it: black silk tea, made from the black silk of an old umbrella, torn in strips and boiled in rain water that had stood in a pan out in the dew all night, to be taken hot the first thing in the morning. Small, green, new potatoes worn in the pocket were excellent for warding off cramps. A solution of chewing-tobacco, kerosene oil and "rotgut" whiskey was a positive guarantee against any kind of stomach disorder, and the correct proportions being known only to himself, he was without conscience when it came to stating a fee for his service. Most extraordinary of all was his cure for bed-wetting; and the number of mothers who could furnish testimonials as to the service rendered to their afflicted children was without limit. The child suffering from this distressing complaint was to be taken to the graveyard at sundown and required to hunt for a crawfish hole on the top of some grave, over which it must sit and perform the baneful nightly habit, at the same time singing the chorus of a hymn designated:

O don't you wor-ry—— O —— don't you wor-ry——

O don't you wor-ry—— Je-sus goin' a-make up my dy-in' bed.

His cures for spells, or "conjured pains and sufferings," were known by such names as "high John the conqueror," "bringing-back turtle-neck dust," "rattlesnake dust," "buzzard nest maiden feathers powder," "lovage root," and "Adam and Eve fix liquor"; but their component parts no one but himself ever knew. His spell for the "wandering foot" never failed once it was put into effect. The person desiring to put this spell on any objectionable party would be required to get by stealth from the party in question, a lock of hair, a finger or toenail paring, and a particle of dead skin; these were brought to Dr. Giles and he would insert them in the hollow of a willow twig from which the pith had been removed. The ends were then sealed with beeswax and the twig was to be buried under the roots of a willow tree growing by the side of running water. Until this twig decayed the "fixed" person was doomed to wander, and only the removal of the twig could break the spell.

Dr. Giles' singing of "If You Can't Come" is a picture of true minstrelsy that is without parallel. He was seated in his rickety old jumper, dressed in a bright red flannel shirt, with his aureole of squirrel tails and tobacco tags, on the foot-rest between his long legs a bunch of squawking chickens, and tied to the axle of the jumper a bundle of coon-skins and artichokes. Gathered around his fantastic chariot were several curious idlers and a group of inquisitive dogs. Dr. Giles had just arrived and announced himself in the usual way, and had sent word in to the barkeeper to have "some stimmalashun" sent out to him, not caring to leave his coon-skins and chickens to the mercy of the investigating dogs and onlookers. After waiting some time for the approach of the comforting refreshment and seeing that it was not forthcoming at the moment, he adjusted himself on the seat of the jumper and began shouting his song of importunity, keeping time on the slats of the rickety jumper floor until his heavy stamping drove his feet through, letting him down on the ground so smoothly and deftly that his song was not disturbed in the least. He continued to call out to the angelic host unperturbed, amid a bewildering chorus of laughing onlookers, barking dogs and squawking chickens; never stopping until he reached the Kingdom of Zion, by which time a colored man from the barroom had arrived with his schooner of beer.

The hymn is very old and is seldom sung unless by some of the older generation.

IF YOU CAN'T COME, SEND ONE ANGEL DOWN

Piano

If a you can't come, If- a you can't come, If a you can't come, Lawd, send a one an gel down. Send him in a hur-ry——

Send him fo' to bring me——— Send him in a

hur - ry, Lawd——— If - a you can't come.———

<table>

II

If-a you can't come,
If-a you can't come,
If-a you can't come, Lawd,
Send-a one angel down.
Send him in de midnight,
Send him in de mawnin',
Send him in a hurry, Lawd,
If-a you can't come.

III

If-a you can't come,
If-a you can't come,
If-a you can't come, Lawd,
Send-a one angel down.
Send him in de lightnin',
Send him in de thunduh,
Send him in a hurry, Lawd,
If-a you can't come.

IV

If-a you can't come,
If-a you can't come,
If-a you can't come, Lawd,
Send-a one angel down.
Send him for a witness,
Send him, a redeemuh,
Send him in a hurry, Lawd,
If-a you can't come.

V

If-a you can't come,
If-a you can't come,
If-a you can't come, Lawd,
Send-a one angel down.
Send him on a rainbow,
Send him in a glory,
Send him in a hurry, Lawd,
If-a you can't come.

VI

If-a you can't come,
If-a you can't come,
If-a you can't come, Lawd,
Send-a one angel down.
Send him fum de kingdom,
Send him ovuh Zion,
Send him in a hurry, Lawd,
If-a you can't come.

</table>

I GOT TWO WINGS

OF all unwelcome days, "blue Monday" was the greatest bug-bear for most madonnas of the wash-tub. To other unimaginative ones it was a sort of Dies Irae; but to Hattie Sparks it came as a day of carolling and exultation, resembling a sort of ceremony with a fixed song-ritual. As soon as you heard her begin to intone her cheerful syncopated version of St. Luke, second chapter, verse nine, you knew that services had begun:

Ask an'-a you shall be giv-en, Seek an' you shall fin',

Knock at de do' an' de do' fly op-en. An'-a love come trick-lin

down, O true be-liev-uh, Love come trick-lin' down.

Without looking to see, you knew that the pale blue reek of smoke was beginning to ascend from the charcoal furnace under the syca-more tree, and all the tubs were filled with water from the cistern, and the clothes were separated, the white pieces in one pile and the colored ones in another, and the rigorous washing ceremony was under way.

Later on you heard the declamatory strains of "I Got Two Wings to Veil My Face," then you knew that the service was in full swing and Hattie was soaring aloft on shining pinions of glory, far away

amid comforting visions of a future life, her thoughts completely removed from the laborious task before her. The splashing of the water
in the tub and the changing iridescence of the soapsuds evoke fancy
after fancy, and the spirit of poetry dominates. With every conscien-
tious rub on the washboard she gives full voice to her exultation.

I GOT TWO WINGS

down to de ri-vuh Jur-den Fo' to res' mah we-a-ry soul.

(2nd Verse)

O hur-ry, an-gel, hur-ry, Lawd I want yuh fo' to hur-ry on down I want yuh to trou-ble de wa-tuh Wid yo' wings an' yo' snow— w'ite gown.

(3rd Verse)

O de sun rose ear-ly in de mawn-in', Went down in de west-un hill, Yuh kin car-ry my name whah-so-e-vuh yuh will yuh got to swal-luh death bit-tuh— pill.

IV

O I heard a mighty rumblin'
    Like de fallin' of de Egyp' race;
O my Lawd got angry in de heaven
    An' de saints turned ovuh in dey place.

(Chorus)

Lawd, I got two wings fo' to veil my face,
I got two wings fo' to fly wid;
I got two wings fo' to veil my face,
I got two wings fo' to fly wid.

HE NEVER SAID A MUMBLIN' WORD

IN spite of his being a faithful adherent of the Baptist tradition, according to his lights, George Riley was without doubt a Christian by night and a pagan by day. It may have been due to his close companionship with old Uncle Andrew, his grandfather, whose ancestral veneration for the sun and the moon and half-remembered strange impossible things had unconsciously awakened in George a faint reverence, in many respects admirable.

His belief in the power of the moon to perform feats of wonder and destruction upon poor defenseless mortals and humble creatures was so intense that he would never venture out of doors bareheaded in the moonlight, even as far as across the yard. If he heard dogs barking, or roosters crowing at night, or if a mocking bird began to sing joyously in some nearby tree, George was sure the moon "was workin' on 'um."

His tales of the sun and its potency were likewise many and marvelous; the most interesting, perhaps, his belief in the myth of the "sun shout" or "sun dance" on Easter Sunday morning. For many years he had tried to witness this remarkable phenomenon, declared by many of his credulous friends to be an actual occurrence, when at last his childish desire was gratified beyond every expectation.

To be awakened every morning by the voice of George administering some apt Scripture quotation, standing by the side of the bed with a demi-tasse of fragrant black coffee and a sprig of honeysuckle or sweet basilique on the saucer, was not an unusual performance; but to be awakened betimes on Easter Sunday morning by something resembling the mild rumble of expostulation from the same ecstatic bringer of the comforting beverage, with a plate full of wild violets and snake strawberries all dripping with dew, was something to make one question the meaning thereof.

The one place where snake strawberries were plentiful was down in the lane leading to the artichoke field; and the only place where wild violets were to be found was under the bridge at the farthest end of the garden. So it was natural to conclude that George was up before daylight and had made an eager pilgrimage to the wild violet bridge to await the coming of the sun and behold the mystical Easter Sunday "shout," as the sun rose above the horizon and looked upon the worshipful earth, dancing for very joy at the Resurrection of the Son of Man.

His happiness was impressive, and the only reply I got to my request for an explanation of the strange event was his admonitory chant:

"Git up fum hyeah
  An' open yo' eye,
  An' give Gawd praise
Dis big Eastuh Sunday mawnin'.

Many a man lay'n flat 'is back,
Can't open 'is eye
To view Gawd ways,—
An' yuh lay'n hyeah
Wid all two yo' eyes,
An' all yo' strank,

Flat on yo' back,—
An' de sun done rose
An' shout an' dance
An' gone on up to glory!"

It was the kind of ecstasy that does not pass quickly. All day long his voice could be heard through the house chanting, "He Never Said a Mumblin' Word," with a spirit that seemed to express a feeling of adulation rather than a feeling of commiseration which the words naturally inspire.

HE NEVER SAID A MUMBLIN' WORD

O they took my bless-ed Lawd — Bless-ed Lawd — Bless-ed Lawd — O they took my bless-ed Lawd — an' He nev-er said a mum-blin' word — Not a word —

III

O they bound Him with a purple cord,
Purple cord, purple cord,
O they bound him with a purple cord,
An' He never said a mumblin' word,
Not a word, not a word, not a word.

IV

O they plaited Him a crown o' thorn,
Crown o' thorn, crown o' thorn,
O they plaited Him a crown o' thorn,
An' He never said a mumblin' word,
Not a word, not a word, not a word.

V

O they put it on His head,
On His head, on His head,
O they put it on His head,
An' He never said a mumblin' word,
Not a word, not a word, not a word.

VI

An' the blood come streamin' down,
Streamin' down, streamin' down,
O the blood come streamin' down,
An' He never said a mumblin' word,
Not a word, not a word, not a word.

VII

An' they judged Him all night long,
All night long, all night long,
Yes they judged Him all night long,
An' He never said a mumblin' word,
Not a word, not a word, not a word.

VIII

An' they whipped Him up the hill,
Up the hill, up the hill,
O they whipped Him up the hill,
An' He never said a mumblin' word,
Not a word, not a word, not a word.

IX

Then they nailed Him to the cross,
To the cross, to the cross,
Yes they nailed Him to the cross,
An' He never said a mumblin' word,
Not a word, not a word, not a word.

X

An' the blood come tricklin' down,
Tricklin' down, tricklin' down,
O the blood come tricklin' down,
An' He never said a mumblin' word,
Not a word, not a word, not a word.

XI

An' the stars refused to shine,
'Fused to shine, 'fused to shine,
Yes the stars refused to shine,
An' He never said a mumblin' word,
Not a word, not a word, not a word.

XII

O wasn't that a pity an' a shame,
Pity an' a shame, pity an' a shame?
O wasn't that a pity an' a shame?
An' He never said a mumblin' word,
Not a word, not a word, not a word.

THAT SUITS ME

NO one ever forgot Bob Moore after once seeing him. He had several distinguishing characteristics by which he would be remembered: his uproarious, ringing laugh, his little gold hoop earrings, and the unusual combination of decided Indian features with an African complexion of true ebony hue.

The colored people all regarded Bob with a little feeling of mistrust because he was connected with the parish affairs and had his headquarters in the court house. He served in various capacities from messenger to keeper of the jail-house keys, but he was known throughout the village as "the dog undertaker," which calling kept him quite occupied during certain weeks of the summer. He held the commission to go about during the season when dogs are supposed to go mad and furnish them with transportation in the form of poisoned sausages, to the waiting realm of Cerberus far beyond the Dog Star. This gruesome performance, of course, was always carried on at night; and as the harvest was invariably a large one, Bob would be seen early the following morning gathering up the slain in his wheelbarrow to roll them down to the Potter's Field, where he buried them at 50 cents each. Needless to say his enemies were many despite his generous nature and his efforts to make merry with them over the barroom counter.

His death was sudden and his funeral pathetic, far from being anything like the childish wish he expressed so often when singing his favorite spiritual, "Dat Suits Me," as he trundled his wheelbarrow of departed village dogs down to their last resting place,—

129

"Wen I die, Lawd, I wanna die right,
　Wanna march up in de Kingdom all dressed in w'ite,
　　Dat suits me."

The day Bob Moore died was cold and dark and rainy. The next day was without rain, but bleak and cold, and the funeral was very late getting away from the church. The service was long and elaborate with song and preaching, and it was nearly six o'clock when they reached the graveyard. The carriage road was so soft and muddy from the hard rain of the day before that it was impossible to drive nearer than within half a block of the front gate, making it necessary to carry the coffin from the hearse to the grave, which was back in a far corner of the cemetery, where it was low and swampy.

They had brought the coffin as far as the graveyard gate when it was discovered that the grave had not been dug and the sexton had not yet arrived and it was growing darker every moment; so the coffin was deposited on the rude crosstie bridge over the gutter at the front gate, and the funeral party went back to town, leaving poor Bob to the loneliness of the night and the watching of the kindly stars.

He was buried next morning without honors or onlookers, in a watery bed in a desolate corner of the Great Samaritan graveyard, just across the street from the Potter's Field with its innumerable weed-grown mounds of unremembered village dogs.

DAT SUITS ME

don' wan'-a fall — Dat suits — me.

(5th Verse)

Wen I die — Lawd I wan-na die right,— Dat suits me.

Wen I die, Lawd I wan-na die right,— Dat suits — me.

Wen I die — Lawd I wan-na die right,— wan-na

maach up in de king-dom all dressed in w'ite,— Dat suits — me.

II

Take kyeah membuhs how you walk on de cross,
 Dat suits me;
Take kyeah membuhs how you walk on de cross,
 Dat suits me;
Take kyeah membuhs how you walk on de cross,
Yo' foot might slip an' yo' soul get los',
 Dat suits me.

III

Come on sistuhs, can't you help me sing,
 Dat suits me;
Come on sistuhs, can't you help me sing,
 Dat suits me;
Come on sistuhs, can't you help me sing,
Dis feelin' in my bosom is a happy thing,
 Dat suits me.

IV

You kin weep like a willuh an' moan like a dove,
 Dat suits me;
You kin weep like a willuh an' moan like a dove,
 Dat suits me;
You kin weep like a willuh an' moan like a dove,
If you wanna git to heaven, you got to go wid love,

O MARY, WHAT YOU WEEPIN' ABOUT?

TO make her work light, Hattie Sparks would get Jennie Miller to help her, taking turn about with the washing and ironing. They were inseparable friends and both of them true lovers of song; and the promise of a pitcher of beer when they came to bring home the laundry never failed to work wonders in the way of getting them to sing for me, whenever there was something new or interesting to hear.

Jennie would sing all night, as long as she felt the "sperret" move her; but Hattie would stop singing the moment she heard Jennie begin to "speak 'uh words twice," which was Hattie's manner of describing Jennie's muddled condition. Unfortunately she had never learned to "tetch de jug light an' drink like people."

Following the natural method common to all colored singers, hardly any melody they sang would be given in simple form, but would be harmonized, with Hattie singing an alto part with a voice as mellow as the sound of a rich reed instrument, and Jennie singing the soprano melody, her voice as sweet and soothing as the tone of an old violin.

133

Excess of spirits of a deleterious nature brought the unfortunate Jennie to an early end. Her funeral was pathetic. Poor Joe, her husband by selection though not by law, kind and devoted as he had been throughout the six years of their happy companionship together, was seen walking alone behind the few carriages in which her family rode to the Great Samaritan graveyard at the back of the town, walking alone, a solitary mourner, a lonely bereaved partner, not wanting to ride because he did not consider himself "one de fam'ly."

Jennie got the song, "O Mary, What You Weepin' About," from her mother, old Aunt Sophie Anatole, who had learned it as a slave on the Millaudon plantation.

O MARY, WHAT YOU WEEPIN' ABOUT?

O Ma-ry wat yuh weep-in' a-bout—
O Ma-ry wat yuh weep-in a-bout,— O Ma-ry wat yuh weep-in' a-bout,— O Lawd, O mah Lawd.
Weep-in' be-cause mah breth-uh is dead,—

Weep-in' be - cause mah breth-uh is dead— weep-in' be-cause mah

breth - uh is dead———— O Lawd, O mah Lawd

(Verses 5, 6.)

Weep not, Ma - ry, You'll see him a gain— Weep not, Ma-ry, you'll—

see him a-gain— Weep not, Mary, you'll see him-a-gain—

O Lawd, O my Lawd. On de Re - sur = rec - tion—

an' de las' day.— On de Re - sur - rec - tion—

an' de las' day.— On de Re - sur - rec - tion—

an' de las' day.——— O Lawd, O my Lawd.

III

O Mary, how long he been dead?
O Mary, how long he been dead?
O Mary, how long he been dead?
 O Lawd, O my Lawd.

IV

Three long days an' three long nights,
Three long days an' three long nights,
Three long days an' three long nights,
 O Lawd, O my Lawd.

VII

By dis time he stinketh in de grave,
By dis time he stinketh in de grave,
By dis time he stinketh in de grave,
 O Lawd, O my Lawd.

VIII

O Mary, come show me de place,
O Mary, come show me de place,
O Mary, come show me de place,
 O Lawd, O my Lawd.

IX

Show me de place whah yo' brethuh lay,
Show me de place whah yo' brethuh lay,
Show me de place whah yo' brethuh lay,
 O Lawd, O my Lawd.

X

Jesus an' Mary walkin' side by side,
Jesus an' Mary walkin' side by side,
Jesus an' Mary walkin' side by side,
 O Lawd, O my Lawd.

XI

Walkin' down to Lazarus' grave,
Walkin' down to Lazarus' grave,
Walkin' down to Lazarus' grave,
 O Lawd, O my Lawd.

XII

Peeped in de grave an' de grave was dahk,
Peeped in de grave an' de grave was dahk,
Peeped in de grave an' de grave was dahk,
 O Lawd, O my Lawd.

XIII

Rise up Laz'rus, walk an' go free,
Rise up Laz'rus, walk an' go free,
Rise up Laz'rus, walk an' go free,
 O Lawd, O my Lawd.

XIV

My Lawd Gawd Jesus done jus' like He said,
My Lawd Gawd Jesus done jus' like He said,
My Lawd Gawd Jesus done jus' like He said,
 O Lawd, O my Lawd.

XV

He healed de sick an' He raised de dead,
He healed de sick an' He raised de dead,
He healed de sick an' He raised de dead,
 O Lawd, O my Lawd.

MY SOUL WANTS TO GO HOME TO GLORY

IT is both curious and interesting to find something of the same spirit pervading the play songs and labor chants entering into many of the devotional songs, with what might be called a sort of reverential gaiety. In no other human, perhaps, is the mingling of pathos and humor more marked than in the Negro, unless it be the Irishman. It is the Negro's complete and continual simplicity that makes him so interesting an art study; his pathetic, naïvely religious quality, his longing with a childish longing for the good things of the world, the mingling of emotions that sounds a rollicking note even when he is sad, and a tragic one when he often means to be funny.

There is a variety of spiritual known as the "contest hymn," which is usually sung at Saturday night song contests at the Baptist churches. A prize is offered, in most cases a basket of groceries, and the singer keeping the floor the longest time is awarded the prize. A man takes the part of questioner and a woman the part of answerer, these two singing the verses of the hymn and the congregation acting as chorus. The man asks the same question again and again, the woman being expected to give a different answer each time, until her imagination becomes exhausted and his questioning vanquishes her. Sometimes three or four singers take the floor, the contest lasting several hours before the winner is chosen.

A fine example of unhampered imagination is shown in this song, "My Soul Wants to Go Home to Glory." It was taken down from the singing of George Riley, who got it in broken portions from the singing of Aunt Lina Batiste, old Aunt Hen'retta Johnson and Lizzie Lane, or "Big Sis," as she was called on account of her great height.

Big Sis was notorious for her singing during the cane-cutting season, when the village Negroes went up to the plantations to cut sugar cane and earn extra money for their New Year celebration, which to

them is a more important holiday than Christmas. The ceremony of the "last stalk of cane," when the cane-field is cleared and the cutting is over, is an occasion of great jubilation with the Negroes; and Big Sis, on account of her impressive size and her fine voice, was always selected as leader. She would take her place at the head of a procession of women on the cane-field, with a long stalk of sugar-cane unstripped of its leaves, in one hand, and her big cane-knife in the other; and all the women, each one with a stalk of sugar-cane and a cane-knife, would follow her up and down through the cane furrows, joining in with her ecstatic singing and going through a series of posturing and gyrations very similar to the rhythmic dancing of the American Indians.

The words of this song were always impromptu; bearing on the growing of the cane, the singing of the wind in the leaves, the heavy frost on the ground in the early November morning, the half-frozen rabbits and wild creatures that sought shelter in among the cane stalks, the diminishing of the cane rows and the ultimate cutting of the last stalk, and the thought of departure for home with a "nice bounty" for New Year jubilation.

I could never get more than a fragment of the song from Big Sis, as she never seemed able to recall the words without the inspiration of the occasion and the cane-field setting with its conducive atmosphere.

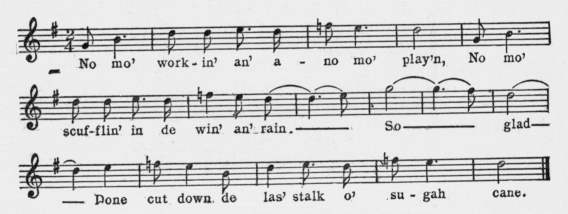

No mo' work-in' an' a - no mo' play'n, No mo'
scuf-flin' in de win' an' rain. — So — glad —
— Done cut down de las' stalk o' su-gah cane.

MY SOUL WANTS TO GO HOME TO GLORY

II

He: O tell me my sistuh, etc.
She: Bin a-drinkin' fum de fountain
  Dat nevuh runs dry,
  An' my soul wants to go home to glory.

(Chorus) Roll an' rock, etc.

III

He: O tell me my sistuh, etc.
She: Bin a-walkin' wid de angels
  An' a-waitin' on my Lawd,
  An' my soul wants to go home to glory.

(Chorus) Roll an' rock, etc.

IV

He: O tell me my sistuh, etc.
She: Bin a-listenin' in de valley
  An' a-lookin' fo' de light,
  An' my soul wants to go home to glory.

(Chorus) Roll an' rock, etc.

V

He: O tell me my sistuh, etc.
She: Bin a-weepin' like a willuh
  An' a-moanin' like a dove,
  An' my soul wants to go home to glory.

(Chorus) Roll an' rock, etc.

VI

He: O tell me my sistuh, etc.
She: Bin a-servin' my Redeemuh
  An' a-singin' roun' de th'one,
  An' my soul wants to go home to glory.

(Chorus) Roll an' rock, etc.

I'M A SOLDIER OF THE CROSS IN THE ARMY OF MY LORD

THIS is one of the spirituals I always remember with great pleasure; for it recalls the extraordinary Sunday morning prayer meetings held at Bett Ellison's house in De Gruy's Lane, "up the coast" on the Mississippi River, about a mile above the town of Gretna.

Every Sunday morning Bett's house,—one of the old slave quarters of plantation days,—was the gathering place of eight or ten church members, mostly men; and to hear their harmonious jubilation and inspired singing of the old-time long meter hymns and "shoutin' praise," was an experience to gain which was well worth the effort of several miles' walk. But I had the advantage of living close by in the "big house," and could stand on the back gallery and look across the yard through the branches of the peach trees in Bett's garden and watch the rhythmic swaying of the singers, listening until the intoxicating monotony compelled me to sing with them; the weird witchery enticing me out beyond the fields of blossoming elder bushes reeking with sweets in the sunlight,—through the shady grove of magnolia and persimmon and giant pecan trees with moss-hung branches, out across the open pasture land brilliant with purple vervain and thistles and the gold of false-valerian,—soaring on the wings of song, far away amid artless, elemental things, in a region of uncontaminated beauty and pastoral dreams.

They seemed never to tire, and their meeting would come to an end only because they were called away to attend the afternoon service at the Evening Star Baptist Church on the banks of Harvey's Canal, where the singing would start anew and extend far into the night.

The spirituals sung at Bett's house at these Sunday meetings were mostly the old-time rocking, incantation-like chants with strong, seductive rhythms and unlimited verses, such as, "If You Can't Come Send One Angel Down," "Wasn't That a Witness for My Lord," "Tall Angel at the Bar" and "Zekul Saw the Wheel"; their potent charm made more positive by the captivating accompaniment of patting feet and humming undertone.

I'M A SOLDIER OF DE CROSS

I'm a sol-dier of de cross in de ah-my o' my Lawd I'm a

sol-dier of de cross in de ah my, O I'm

boun' to be a sol-dier in de ah-my o' my Lawd, O I'm

II

I stahted out fo' heaven in de ahmy o' my Lawd,
I stahted out fo' heaven in de ahmy;
An' I'm boun' to be a soldiuh in de ahmy o' my Lawd,
O' I'm boun' to be a soldiuh in de ahmy.

(Chorus)—In de kingdom,
          Wid my Redeemuh,
          Got salvashun
          To bring me ovuh.

III

I'm fightin' fo' my Jesus in de ahmy o' my Lawd,
I'm fightin' fo' my Jesus in de ahmy;
An' I'm boun' to be a soldiuh in de ahmy o' my Lawd,
O' I'm boun' to be a soldiuh in de ahmy.

TOLL THE BELL, ANGEL, I JUST GOT OVER

THERE is a slight similarity between the chorus of this hymn and the chorus of the old Jubilee hymn reading:

"Come down, angels, trouble the water,
Come down, angels, trouble the water,
Come down, angels, trouble the water,
Let God's saints come in."

If this be the original, the present version is an improvement both in words and music.

The singer of this was Nelson Davis, a lad of about fifteen, who, previous to his joining the church, was a pastmaster of pranks and deviltry and the admired leader of all the mischievous boys of the neighborhood.

The thought of his becoming a full-fledged church member was never considered seriously until one morning when every doubt was dispelled by a telephone message from Liza, his mother, asking for a pair of "ole w'ite pants fo' Nelson to be baptize' in." His sister Emmaleet was lavish in her praise of his ability as a singer, and dilated on his religious propensities and how he "made people set up in church fo' true wen 'e staht to make music in de buildin' on Sunday night."

Nelson became a Christian and a song leader of importance and gave no small promise of a worthy career; but he was fated to pass away the following spring and was numbered among the innumerable lesser song-birds that "die with their exquisite melodies in them."

His interpretative power in singing "Toll de Bell, Angel, I Jus' Got Over" was very remarkable in one so young.   He was able to convey all the ancestral fearlessness and fatalism expressed in the melody and the transitional nobility and resignation of spirit gained through super-imposed Christianity, so evident in the refrain, interpreting the distinct emotions with such correct shading and understanding that his listeners experienced a genuine thrill.

TOLL DE BELL, ANGEL, I JUS' GOT OVER

Wen I lay my bo - dy down— Aye Lawd, in de grave - yahd Wen I lay my bo - dy down. Aye Lawd, in de grave - yahd You think you hyeah my

jus' got o - vuh, Well I jus' got o - vuh at las'.——

2nd Verse
Gwin - a lay in de grave an' stretch out my ahm.——

Ay Lawd, in de grave yahd, Lay in de grave an'

stretch out my ahm.—— Ay Lawd, in de grave yahd, Gwin - a

feel so glad I ain' had to wait long,—— Gwin - a

lif' up my voice an' shout - a my song——

Ay Lawd, sing - in' in de grave - yahd.

HEAVEN

IN the new edition of "The Religious Folk Songs of the Negro as Sung on the Plantations," published by the Hampton Institute of Hampton, Virginia, this spiritual will be found under the title "Going to Shout All Over God's Heaven"; also in the collection of Plantation Songs of the Calhoun Colored School of Calhoun, Alabama, it has this title. In various sections of the South it is known as "All God's Chillun Got Wings," and is a great favorite. In every collection in which I have seen it, it is always written in a major key. The version given here, taken down from the singing of George Riley, is the only version I have ever heard sung in a minor key. There are several reasons to believe that it was original with him. Aside from himself and a few members of his family who sang it as he did, I have never known anybody else sing it to a minor melody. The verses are the same as given in the other versions, a slight difference being in the words of the refrain.

HEAVEN

I got a robe, an' you got a robe, An' all my Gawd's chil-lun got a robe —— An' wen I git to hea-ven goin-a

put on my robe, An' shout all   o-vuh Gawd's heav'n—

Hea-v'n——— sweet hea-v'n———   Ev-y-bo-dy

talk-in' bout heav'n not go-in' to— hea-v'n———— Sweet

hea-v'n———— Goin-a shout all   o-vuh Gawd's heav'n.—

II

I got a crown, an' you got a crown,
An' all my Gawd's chillun got a crown;
An' wen I git to heav'n goin'-a put on my crown,
An' shout all ovuh Gawd's heav'n.

(Chorus) Heav'n, sweet heav'n,
            Evybody talkin' 'bout heav'n
            Not goin' to heav'n, sweet heav'n,
            Goin'-a shout all ovuh Gawd's heav'n.

III

I got-a shoes, an' you got-a shoes,
An' all my Gawd's chillun got-a shoes;
An' wen I git to heav'n goin'-a put on my shoes,
An' walk all ovuh Gawd's heav'n.

(Chorus) Heav'n, etc.

IV

I got a hawp, an' you got a hawp,
An' all my Gawd's people got a hawp;
An' wen I git to heav'n goin'-a play on my hawp,
An' shout all ovuh Gawd's heav'n.

(Chorus) Heav'n, etc.

V

I got a song, an' you got a song,
An' all my Gawd's people got a song;
An' wen I git to heav'n goin'-a sing-a my song,
An' shout all ovuh Gawd's heav'n.

(Chorus) Heav'n, etc.

LITTLE DAVID, PLAY ON YOUR HARP

RIDING home in a street car very late on a dank, foggy night in autumn, wondering how I would be able to distinguish the familiar crêpe myrtle and camphor trees at my street corner in the dense fog bank that hid everything, presently my mood was interrupted by the car making a sudden stop; and from somewhere out of the fluid darkness, a weird old colored man appeared and boarded the car. He wore a tattered rabbit-skin cap, an old gray coat of strange cut and generous proportions, and jean trousers so patched and mended with a variety of materials as to give the impression of a derelict quilt. His bushy gray beard was dripping with fog, and his eyes were so bright with seeming merriment they invited a smile from all the passengers who turned to look at him as he entered.

After seating himself comfortably in the end corner of the car, he drew from his coat pocket a set of "quills", or Pan-pipes, made of cane-reed, and after a preliminary scale or two, he began playing upon them in the most entrancing manner, like an ancient black faun in disguise.

Every passenger seemed captivated by the merry lilt of the unexpected minstrelsy. Nothing appeared important but the delight of the moment, inspired by the nameless charm of the sylvan melody. Everything was forgotten,—even my street corner, beyond which I had gone a long distance, though without the slightest regret.

This was how I first heard the music of "L'il David, Play On Yo' Hawp." One or two variants are to be found in some of the well-known collections of Negro spirituals, but I prefer to regard this version as the original one; having heard it as I did, played by a veritable black Pan, appearing mysteriously out of a dense fog and the clustering foliage of bamboos, palms and oleanders bordering the retired avenue of a quaint old city, bringing with him a snatch of melody to charm a street car full of modern passengers, as we are told the elder Pan used to charm the happy, peaceful people of the forest and grove when he trilled to them upon his magic pipes in the old, far-distant days.

There are also different verses; these, the same as those used by the Hampton Students, are given preference.

LI'L DAVID, PLAY ON YO' HAWP

hail Lawd, Loose my peo-ple hail Lawd, Li'l Da-vid, play on—

— yo' hawp, hal - le - lu, hal - le - lu, Li'l Da - vid

play on— yo' hawp, hal - le - lu.

II

Down in de valley,
Hail Lawd,
Did'n wan' stay,
Hail Lawd,
My soul got happy,
Hail Lawd,
I stayed all day,
Hail Lawd.

III

Go down, angel,
Hail Lawd,
Wid ink an' pen,
Hail Lawd,
Write salvashun,
Hail Lawd,
Fo' dyin' men,
Hail Lawd.

(Chorus) Li'l David, play on yo' hawp, etc.

THE OLD MULE

MANY years before the songs "Casey Jones" and "Steamboat Bill" were heard on the vaudeville stage and became popular throughout the country, a melody almost identical was sung by the Negroes in various sections of the South. I recall how great was my surprise the first time I heard the song "Casey Jones," because of the fact that several years previously I had taken down the song of "De Ole Mule" from the singing of a young colored man called Willie, the only name by which he seemed to be known to any one.

During the high-water stage of the Mississippi River the levees are guarded day and night in the towns wherever there are weak spots which might cave in and thereby cause a crevasse. This colored man called Willie was one of the guards at night, and every evening he would come to the "big house" for a jug of drinking water. He was a tall, gaunt young man, over six feet high, with bushy, kinky hair, clothes which appeared to be several sizes too short for him, and accoutered after the fashion of a true minstrel, he never wandered forth without his trusty banjo.

His nightly visit for water was always a welcome one; and after being greeted with a cup of hot coffee and smiles of encouragement from each member of the family, he forthwith expressed his appreciation by taking a seat on the back gallery and singing his quaint songs and ballads for us, to a banjo accompaniment nothing short of ravishing.

The memory of him sitting there in the moonlight, the queer

shadows of his lank form dancing on the gallery floor, the strange hilarious spell his jangling banjo threw about us, the wholesome laughter of George and Angeline and Aunt Elvirah and all the other colored people from the long house in the yard, lured away from home to sit on the steps and sway to the enchantment of Willie's singing,—it is more like a dream fancy than an actual memory; an unforgettable experience to look back on with melancholy pleasure, knowing it can never be lived again.

Whether it is the intrinsic merit of the song, the potent magic of the summer moonlight, the mysterious power of Willie the singer, or the conjuring nature of his banjo music, he seems to stand out

> One of nature's artless minstrels
> Reckless of his way,
> Laudable as early bird-song
> And the laughing day.

In the accompaniment to this song I have tried to give some impression of the banjo, and the jolting of the old wagon with its creaking springs as old Aunt Dinah journeyed down the road urging her weary mule onward. It is but a poor imitation of Willie's charming pastoral humoresque.

DE OLE MULE

Ole Aunt Di-nah had a raw-bone mule,

Got up one mawn-in' wen de air was cool—

Hitched him to de wag-on an' wat she do.—

Staht - ed down de road— fo' de bah - be - cue— An' de ole mule hol - luh bow-wow— Anh-huh, anh-huh, Lawd he hol - luh, Ole mule hol - luh bow-wow—Wid a mouf chock full o' rope.

II

Ole Aunt Dinah goin' down de road,
Ole mule pullin' 'ginse a mighty load;
Sun goin' ovuh to'ards de end o' day,—
Bahbecue way yondah futhuh away.

(Chorus) An' de ole mule holluh, etc.

III

Hawse-fly settin' on a punkin' vine,
Lit on de mule an' bit 'is tail behin';
Mule kicked up an' de dash-boahd bus',—
Yondah come Aunt Dinah rollin' down in de dus'.

(Chorus) An' den de ole mule holluh, etc.

MY BABY IN A GUINEA-BLUE GOWN

THE melody of this song is one of those vagrant airs of the gypsydom of folk-music. It has several variants, each one sung to a different set of words. The set claiming the honor of original place would seem to be the one reading:

> "Mama brought-a me coffee,
> Mama brought-a me tea,
> Mama brought me evvything, babe,
> But de jail-house key;
>   O turn me over, turn me slow.

> "Turn me over easy,
> Turn me over slow;
> Turn me over easy, babe,
> 'Cause de bullets hurt me so;
>   O turn me over, turn me slow."

I was never able to procure more than these two stanzas. Unmistakably it is the record of some tragic happening; and after the established manner of this form of song-ballad, there must have been stanzas of some length telling the story with charming wealth of detail.

The Guinea-blue gown of the lady in the ballad is made of a kind of cotton dress-goods much favored by the Negroes of the South, especially in Louisiana. It is of a dark indigo-blue background with figures or white stripes, and is known by its commercial name "Guinea-blue."

The love story this ballad relates has a pastoral quality truly delightful. The bold gallantry of the young lover, his pleasant pilgrimage with the unknown lady over the pasture and through the lane, his intrepid return visit, his disappointment, his determination to recover the lady of the Guinea-blue glamour, his long journeys to the various rural regions, and his final unsuspected reward, all so typical, and related with such artless simplicity, entitle the song to more than passing commendation.

MY BABY IN A GUINEA-BLUE GOWN

O I ain' gwine stay— no lon - guh, Gwine-a pack mah bun - dle an' go, 'Cause way o - vuh yon - dah in a gui - nea blue gown Dey got a la - dy I use to know, O git yuh read - y in de

maw - nin', I'm go- in' a - way— To mah ba-by in a

gui - nea blue gown.—

(2nd Verse)

I met de la - dy one eve - nin', She was

goin' home all a - lone— I say you bet-tuh lem-me come an'

go long fo' comp-ny an' I cah'y you thoo de dahk clean

home, O git you read-y in de maw-nin' I'm go-in' a - way

— to my ba-by in a Gui - nea blue gown.—

III

I cah'y'd de lady thoo de pastuh,
    I cah'y'd 'uh thoo de puckawn lane,
I cah'y'd 'uh thoo de dahk to 'uh own front do'
    An' she nevuh even tol' me 'uh name.
        O git you ready in de mawnin',
        I'm goin' away to my baby in a guinea-blue gown.

IV

So I went straight back de nex' mawnin',
    An' I ax fo' de lady right plain,
But dey tol' me dat de lady done gone in de fiel'
    Whah de wimmins was cuttin' cane.
        O git you ready in de mawnin',
        I'm goin' away to my baby in a guinea-blue gown.

V

So I went down yondah to de cane-fiel'
    An' I looked all up an' down,
An' I axed all de wimmins an' dey say dey ain' seen
    No lady in a guinea-blue gown.
        O git you ready in de mawnin',
        I'm goin' away to my baby in a guinea-blue gown.

VI

Den I crossed ovuh yondah to de bayou
    Whah de mens was pickin' moss,
But I ain' seen de lady dah no whah roun',
    An' I say, well she mus' be los'.
        O git you ready in de mawnin',
        I'm goin' away to my baby in a guinea-blue gown.

VII

But I kep' on huntin' till de evenin',
    An' I tell you I sho felt so'e;
But wen I got home, Lawd! de lady was a-waitin' fo' me
    Yondah at my own front do'.
        O git you ready in de mawnin',
        I'm goin' away to my baby in a guinea-blue gown.

GRUMBELLIN' PEOPLE

NOTWITHSTANDING the serious attention given to the subject by many curious investigators, no one was fortunate in arriving at a satisfactory explanation of the name Caah-tahn, the only name by which this eccentric character was known to all his "felluh constit-yunts." Perhaps Quartien was the dignified Creole original, a name possible of being conferred during old plantation days when he was a field-hand, a "quartien," or dweller in the quarters. Also it may be derived from "quartant," meaning a quarter of a cask, which amount would seem a fair estimate of the quantity he could accommodate with comfort during his periodical revels on "sour wine," as he called the cheap grade of claret he bought from "Mistuh Honnus groc'ry sto'."

Caahtahn was the phonetic pronunciation of the name as given by the Negroes, and it was the only family name or "direck intitlus" he seemed to possess. He also answered to the nickname Sugarfoot, given to him because of the afflicted condition of his pedal extremities. The apparent mystery surrounding him helped to make him the picturesque character he was. No one appeared to have any knowledge regarding his parentage or the section from whence he came. Some said he "b'lonked to Plaquemine Parish," and that his feet had been frost-bitten in the cane-field where he worked as a boy, due to which he had never been able to wear shoes; and others said that he had come from Bayou Lafourche and that he had ill-treated his mother when he was a young man, and she had "put a bad wish on him" and "cussed" him, swearing that he would never wear shoes as long as he lived, which was the reason he always went barefooted, even in the coldest weather.

Caahtahn revealed nothing, but kept his dark secret and went his pleasant rounds disregardful of any conjecture about his past history or his present fame, always amusing, and especially entertaining "when the wine was in." The long bench under the shed at "Mistuh Honnus" corner grocery store was his favorite camping ground. He could be found there almost any time, with his porringer of "ham trimmin's an' brown suguh," a five-cent portion of each in brown paper, spread out before him on the bench where he sat astride, with his back against the post, munching with the supreme satisfied air of one at a feast and singing between bites his snatches of "play-song" and "random," to the great amusement of his little crowd of admiring listeners. Sometimes his menu would be elaborated with a "nickel wuth o' 'Mericun cheese" or a "can o' cundense' milk," which luxuries he was permitted to indulge in only when he had succeeded in collecting an extra nickel or two from passing "w'ite-folks" who stopped to hear his whimsical recital and enjoy his awkward shuffling dance movements performed for their special benefit.

His crude minstrelsy consisted of fragments of song and verse strung together indiscriminately, with no sense of coherence but always rhythmic and melodious. Like good old Omar Khayyam who was "never deep in anything but wine," Caahtahn was a living interpretation of the lines,

> "Wine dispenses into air
> Selfish thoughts and selfish care."

His voice like his outlook on life was cheerful though unconvincing, but his performances were superb, especially after generous potations. He would sing a few bars of melody, then intone several lines to one note, then sing a few more bars, ending with a kind of recitative given in a high-pitched voice as near falsetto as his deep baritone permitted him to affect. A great favorite with small children was a short song he called "Jo-buh-see-bus":

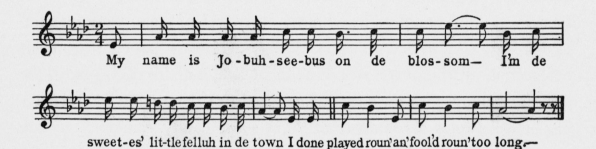

My name is Jo-buh-see-bus on de blos-som— I'm de
sweet-es' lit-tle felluh in de town I done played roun' an' fool'd roun' too long.—

(*Spoken*): Hop light, boys, de Yankees comin'!

This last exclamation was given with gestures and a movement of the body suggesting a man on horseback urging his horse into a gallop to escape being captured by the imaginary pursuers, the "Yankees."

Another curious bit of entertainment was his recital of "Reb'-time" history:

> "Eighteen-hunded an' sixty-one,
> Das de yeah de wah begun;
> Eighteen-hunded an' sixty-two,
> I was fightin' an' so was you;
> Eighteen-hunded an' sixty-three,
> Ab'aham Lincoln set de nigguhs free;

> Eighteen-hunded an' sixty-fo',
> Peace proclaim' fo' to fight no mo';
> Eighteen-hunded an' sixty-five,
> Nigguhs all happy fo' to be alive."

After a program of such fragments as these, Caahtahn would sing his song of the hog and the sheep, his philosophical observations of life which he called "Grumbellin' People." This was the only lengthy song he was ever known to give.

GRUMBELLIN' PEOPLE

Hog an' a sheep was a walk-in' -in de pas - tuh Says de

hog to de sheep can't you walk a lit - tle fas - tuh. —

Lawd, Lawd, da's de way — things be.

sat - a - fied. Things kin be— don' kyeah how fine— You hyeah folks grum-bel-lin' all de time,—— Lawd, Lawd, I won-duh wat make—it be.—

II

I got a new frock wid-out a single thing a-missin',
You keep a-grudgin' 'cause it looks a little bettuh'n dis'un,—
Lawd, Lawd, das de way things be.
Das des de reason we's a unpuhtecded nigguh nation,
All time begrudgin' one anothuh out dey situation,—
Lawd, Lawd, I wonduh wat make it be.

(Chorus) Das de way things be divide,
People don' nevuh seem satafied;
Things kin be don' kyeah how fine,
You hyeah folks grumbellin' all de time.
Lawd, Lawd, I wonduh wat make it be.

HONEY BABY

THIS song has much of the primitive essence of that untaught and unteachable creative art through which the half-inarticulate and groping mind of the Negro reveals itself. Song is his natural and therefore easiest means of self-expression, coloring every phase of his life, evoking memorials of hope and happiness in his brighter moments, and glorifying the dolent sighs and sorrows that fold him about with shadows.

It is one of those vagrant love laments composed by no one in particular and by every one in general. It gives an interesting picture of a lonely lover working out in the gloomy cypress swamp, separated from the lady of his choice and the many "creature comforts" which make his humble home his goodly kingdom. The long-looked-for and never-received "letter from down the road" brings added weight to his loneliness, and the remembered talents and virtues of his worthy home companion fill him with eagerness to return to her. The chorus with its importunate appeal to the "Miss Exchange-Lady" to give ear to the urgent long-distance message to his dusky Dulcinea of the big East Green, may go back as far as the day when the wonder of long-distance telephoning was a subject of great moment among the people of rural districts where telephones were innovations inspiring fear and bewilderment; likewise machines of undisputed miraculous character to the childish mind of a Negro worker in the lonely cypress swamp. It may also date to the time when the popular ballads of Charles K. Harris and other song-writers of his school were being sung everywhere, and the song "Hello, Central, Give Me Heaven" may have suggested the telephone idea.

It was sung and whistled by the Negroes of the East Green in Gretna and I got it in broken parts from Hattie Sparks, Michel Clay and a colored man called Cunjuh. By reconstructing the whole with the assistance of George Riley, who, though he denounced it as a "sinful ballet" and was not in sympathy with my interest in it, I was enabled to arrive at a version very close to the original through his memory of having heard it sung frequently on the streets and at meetings where "levity was free and in the ascendant."

HONEY BABY

O dey ain' but one thing a-troub-lin' my min'. But one thing a troub-lin' me — all o' de time, Says I won-duh whah— is my hon-ey ba-by gone.

It's but one peo-ple I'm griev-in' to see, O my

hon - ey ba - by is you griev - in' fo' me, Lawd I

ain' wish fo' comp-'ny like I'm wish in' now since I bin bawn

(Chorus)

'Cause my hon - ey ba - by, says yo' pa-pa ain' mad wid

you ——————— 'Cause you done done fo' me wat no yuth-uh oo-man kin

do. ——————— I'm gwine go down yon-dah to de w'ite folks pot-a-ker-ry

foam. ————— An' ax 'um fo' to tell you dat I'm staht-in' on my jour-ney home. —————

(2d Verse)
(And Chorus for last verse)

I tell you, peo - ple, says my troub - les is hahd, My

ba - by way— yon - dah in a - yuth-uh peo - ple yahd, An'

me hyeah wait - in' fo' a let - tuh fum down de road.——

So my hon-ey ba-by put de pot on de hook I got a
might-y ap-pa-tite fo' wat some-ev-uh you cook, Lawd I'm
mos done— played out fum toat-in' dis tuh-bul load.—
(Chorus) O Hel-lo, Cent-ul, won't you gim-me long dist-un
foam— O Miss Ex-change la-dy won't you gim-me long dist-un
foam— O please young la-dy won't you gim-me long dist-un foam— I wan
foam to my ba-by dat I'm staht-in on my journ-ey home.—

III

O I lef' my baby 'cause she treated me mean
Yondah in my kingdom in de big Eas' Green,
    But I can' keep fum thinkin' 'bout my baby dese couple o' days.
'Cause my baby's a seamstuh, she kin wash, an' st'yew,
She's a natchal-bawn workin' ooman thoo'-an'-thoo,
    She's a gal fum my home but she cert'ny got low-down ways.

(Spoken: But inny-how, I can' he'p sayin:)

(Chorus) O my honey-baby, says yo' papa ain' mad wid you,
    'Cause you done done fo' me wat no yuthuh ooman kin do.
    I'm gwine down yondah to de w'ite folks potakerry foam
    An' ax 'um fo' to tell you dat I'm stahtin' on my journey home.

(Additional chorus after third verse)

(Spoken: I'm gwine say:)

IV

Hello Centul, won't you gimme long distun foam?
O Miss Exchange-lady, won't you gimme long distun foam?
O please young lady, won't you gimme long distun foam,—
I wan' foam to my baby dat I'm stahtin' on my journey home.